TOSHIBA

This book is the fourth in the series *Japanese Business: The Human Face*, which will examine the most important companies in Japan today. These companies are all global leaders with multi-billion dollar turnovers and thousands of employees. Yet they face unprecedented challenges in the next few years. The pace of globalization, technical development, consumer expectation and growing international competition has never been faster. This series shows how the best and most successful are adapting and changing to remain in front. Each book describes the company's strategy, organizational code and the role of its leadership in steering each company to continued success. These books contain crucial lessons for anyone interested in organizations, business and managing change.

Titles published in the series *Japanese Business: The Human Face*

JAPANESE BUSINESS
THE HUMAN FACE

TOSHIBA

Defining a New Tomorrow

ROBERT L. CUTTS

PENGUIN BOOKS

Published by the Penguin Group

Penguin Books Ltd, 80 Strand, London WC2R ORL, England

Penguin Putnam Inc., 375 Hudson Street, New York, New York 10014, USA

Penguin Books Australia Ltd, 250 Camberwell Road, Camberwell, Victoria 3124, Australia

Penguin Books Canada Ltd, 10 Alcorn Avenue, Toronto, Ontario, Canada M4V 3B2

Penguin Books India (P) Ltd, 11, Community Centre, Panchsheel Park, New Delhi – 110 017, India

Penguin Books (NZ) Ltd, Cnr Rosedale and Airborne Roads, Albany, Auckland, New Zealand

Penguin Books (South Africa) (Pty) Ltd, 24 Sturdee Avenue, Rosebank 2196, South Africa

Penguin Books Ltd, Registered Offices: 80 Strand, London WC2R ORL, England

www.penguin.com

First published 2002

1

Set in 11.5/14 pt Monotype Bembo
Typeset by Rowland Phototypesetting Ltd, Bury St Edmunds, Suffolk
Printed and bound in Great Britain by Clays Ltd, St Ives plc

ISBN 0-713-99636-6

Contents

Foreword

It is a great privilege to be admitted to the inner councils of a corporate giant such as Toshiba, and to be given the freedom to pursue a virtually unbounded range of subjects with so many interviewees, of all ranks. I would like at the beginning of this book to especially thank both Chairman Taizo Nishimuro and President Tadashi Okamura for the generous amounts of time they have each given me, and for the candor and thoughtfulness of their replies to my questions.

The background of this author is journalism, and I make no claim to having produced a scholarly study of Toshiba in these pages. Rather, my intent has been to convey to general readers the air of excitement, creativity, commitment and challenge that animates Toshiba, and how vital these qualities are to all levels of its management and effort, especially in these opening years of the twenty-first century.

My hope is that the reader will find here coherent answers to the questions that I myself set out with when I began this work: how does an enormous organization like Toshiba do all the things it does so well, and what does it hope to move forward to in the global age?

I owe thanks to all the interviewees named herein, and many more people inside and outside Toshiba as well. I was given much help by Katsufumi Nomura, Shigeyuki Miyazaki, Kenichi Sugiyama, Midori Suzuki, and Gareth Pughe of the Toshiba corporate headquarters staff.

Special thanks are also due to Eithne Jones, Yasuhiko Shibat-suji, Mark Schreiber, Chris Harrington, Marilee Swirczek, Elton Southard and the library staffs of the Foreign Correspondents Club and the International House, both in Tokyo.

Of course, all errors are the responsibility of the author, not of those persons generous enough to have given him so much help.

This work is the result of extensive research throughout 2001, with a major portion of key interviews conducted in Japan during the summer.

In this work I have chosen somewhat arbitrarily to translate, with some historical exceptions, all yen figures into dollars at the rate of 120 yen = 1 US dollar, a ratio close to that which obtained through the middle of 2001. I have applied the Western and not the Japanese style for personal names: first names are followed by family names.

Robert L. Cutts
Tokyo, March 2002

PART ONE

CHAPTER ONE
ALL THE VIBRANT VOICES

The multipurpose corporation that is emerging demands, among other things, smarter executives. It implies a management capable of specifying multiple goals, weighting them, interrelating them, and finding . . . policies that optimize not for one, but for several variables simultaneously.

The Third Wave
Alvin Toffler
(Wm. Morrow & Co., New York, 1980)

Shogo Yamada was nothing if not a salesman. In 1950, nearing the end of the blighted days of the Occupation of his country, he traveled Japan for his employer Toshiba trying to sell, of all things, washing machines. Few families in that day could afford them. But as he made his pitches Yamada kept an eye open for new product ideas, the kind that might let him build new business.

He knew from talking with hundreds of them that Japanese housewives, exposed to magazine and newspaper images of a new life in postwar American homes, were growing more aware and more covetous of the marvelous appliances that could save so much time and work for the lady of the house.

Then it came to him: a common sight he had seen in every neighborhood, everywhere he went in Japan, *was* his opportunity: women laboriously boiling rice, the three-meals-per-day staple, just the way it had been boiled for centuries – in big kettles, over open, wood-burning hearths that had to be constantly hand-tended, in smoky kitchens half-open to the elements.

An automatic, electric rice cooker. That's what the country needed.

He took the idea back to his boss. Though Toshiba, an electric-industries giant, was suffering grievously in the postwar depression and needed something new and low-priced to galvanize its market, it was difficult to convince the company's management. But Yamada did not give up.

One day into Yamada's Tokyo office walked Yoshitada Minami, owner of a tiny electrical plant that was quietly going broke in the cluttered warrens of the city's suburbs. Minami was desperate for subcontracting work. Yamada decided to offer him a deal: you make me an automatic electric rice cooker, and I'll sell it.

It took Minami and his wife, working in their own kitchen, five full years to perfect the Toshiba rice cooker. It wasn't easy: they began by conducting over a thousand experiments in four months just to find the perfect temperature for cooking rice. They quickly ran through their own national rations of rice, and had to put their home in hock for enough cash to buy more grain on the black market.

The plug-in appliance had to quickly heat the water in which the rice soaked to 100 degrees centigrade – boiling – hold it precisely there so that the rice cooked but did not scorch, and shut itself off, all this whether the task was performed in the warm subtropic sun of Okinawa, or the icy blizzards of subarctic Hokkaido.

At last it was perfected. Yamada took the new *Jido Denki-gama* (automatic electric cooker) bearing Toshiba's brand to market himself, hawking it everywhere for the same price: eight dollars and eighty-eight cents.

Within two years he'd sold a million. Within seven years one of every two households in Japan owned one.

It was the hallmark product of the beginning of the end of Japan's darkness of defeat, and the start of its championship as a nation of great manufacturers. Virtually every Japanese over age 50 remembers the first Toshiba rice cooker. Many still use it.

It may seem an insignificant product with which to introduce the story of Toshiba, the 127-year-old Japanese behemoth known for electrification of Japan, for building locomotives and commuter trains and the railway systems they run on, for turning out some of the biggest dynamos and generators in the world, for erecting nuclear power plants and producing the nation's very first light bulbs, for being the No. 2 maker of microchips and the seventh largest integrated electrical and electronics manufacturer in the world.

The humble rice cooker started as a stroke of Toshiba vision, was devised into a product by considering the real needs of its potential customers, was perfected through meticulous testing and reworking, and fulfilled more than one goal: it emerged not only as a product that changed the life of the nation, but also as one that symbolized in all those homes the leading role in Japan's industrial transformation that Toshiba had played since the days of national modernization, and still plays today.

Like the wide-screen TVs you watch, the hard-drive disk in your portable computer, and the DVD digital movie disk player in your home, the electric rice cooker was a signature achievement for Toshiba.

To tell the whole tale of Toshiba is impossible: 188,000 people around the world, making and selling about 50 billion dollars' worth of goods in a year.

To tell the story that *is* possible, of where Toshiba came from, why it exists, and where it is going – and what that means to the world – is difficult. Like assembling the sweeping image of a great classical mosaic, it has to be done one careful piece at a time.

A piece at a time because there are so many stories that make up Toshiba.

Carefully, because they are the stories of individuals and not just an organization. The best way for the reader to get to know the Toshiba story that can be told is to hear it directly from the people who live it each day. You will meet many of them in the pages that follow: a few are geniuses, some are everyday heroes, all of them are good at what they do because they love to do it.

Toshiba began at the confluence of two corporate streams, both of which rose in the heady days of the late 1800s, in the modernization of Meiji Japan. Hisashige Tanaka, called by some "Japan's Edison," was a child prodigy who, though he lived in the deep countryside of then-shogunal Japan, invented a water pump for fire-fighting and a "perpetual" clock.[1] In the service of his feudal lord he helped in the local manufacture of rifles, cannons, and ships' boilers. Soon after the Meiji Restoration that began the industrial transformation of the country, the government opened a telegraph-equipment factory and summoned Tanaka, a man already 76 years old, to Tokyo to build its machinery.

In 1875 he left that work to establish his own company, which spread into the production of heavier electrical equipment such as motors and transformers. In 1904 the company became Shibaura Engineering Works, named for the area of Tokyo Bay industrial quays where it was located.

In 1890 a professor of the Imperial College of Engineering in Tokyo, Ichisuke Fujioka, created Hakunetsu-sha, what would become Tokyo Electric Co., which produced Japan's first incandescent light bulb. The two firms were eventually merged in 1939 into Tokyo Shibaura Electric Co., Ltd., which took the present combi-name of Toshiba Corp. in 1978. Since the postwar period Toshiba has been part of the Mitsui group of loosely linked, large corporations known as *keiretsu*, an arrangement that often involves cross-shareholding and a degree of business cooperation between members.

Toshiba's nine top shareholders today are (in order of holdings) the Sumitomo-Mitsui Bank, Dai-Ichi Life Insurance, Nippon Life Insurance, Japan Trustee Services bank, State Street Bank & Trust, Chase Manhattan Bank (London), Employees' Stock-holding plans, Nihon-Koa Insurance, and Mitsubishi Trust. None holds more than 3.9%; there is no element of family control. Foreigners accounted for 25.4% of shareholders in mid 2001.[2]

From Japan's first electric fan to its first X-ray tube, from its first 3-phase AC power generator to its first 10-ton electric locomotive, from its first fluorescent lamps to its first satellite transmitter, Toshiba has designed and/or manufactured an enormous list of the products that built Japan as a modern nation, and help keep it the world's second largest economy even today.

But as many analysts of modern Japanese economic history have noted, it was not just raw determination and fortuitous capital investment that made this Toshiba. There are, side by side with it, Hitachi, Matsushita Electrical Industrial, Mitsubishi Electric, Fujitsu, NEC, and Oki Electric, all making in lesser and greater combinations and scales pretty much the same major products that Toshiba makes – all of them giant Japanese competitors, all with their roots in the prewar past.

How could they *all* have survived the grinding decades of struggle for market share, even in a fast-growing economy like Japan's?

The answer, of course, lies in great part in the century

of management of the economy by government. "Controlled competition" is what the economic commentator Martin Fransman has labeled it. "[Several financial] crises from 1927 onwards ... through the pressure they put on government budgets, provoked attempts to reduce government costs ... [one solution] was to increase the technological competences of domestic equipment suppliers, while at the same time increasing the competition between them ... to hold down prices and increase quality."[3]

That is, the situation of multiple competitors at almost every level was sponsored, sustained, and managed by what was in effect their best customer, the government, both to keep the companies healthy by developing technical skills and new technologies for sale at fiercely competitive prices – and to keep production domestic (protectionism played a large part in this scheme for many decades, before and after the war).

An echo of these policies is found in modern times. Many main-class Japanese manufacturers like these grew as integrated producers, making components and parts and whole products in many different lines themselves. Especially as they became large-scale exporters (Toshiba's overseas sales ratio today is 37%), the wide number of fields they dominated allowed them to ride out cyclical ups and downs in individual sector markets, whether at home or abroad. When one product line was in down cycle, another would likely be in up cycle.

Toshiba itself enjoyed the added advantage, both pre- and postwar, of technical cooperation, capital tie-ups, and licensing agreements with General Electric of the US, and so had a steady stream of new product concepts and technologies in its "cupboard." (GE was a major Toshiba shareholder both before and after the Great Pacific War, and the two still cooperate as independent partners today, mainly in system control technologies and nuclear energy plants.)

The rapid globalization of Toshiba's markets, bringing the need to procure more capital internationally and to spread manufacturing among many foreign bases quickly, has begun to crumble the old base of domestic strength that national policies created. But we will see below just how the fierce competition that still goes on among these old rivals (not to mention the Sony, Sharp, and Canon entrants of the postwar age) in Japan, as well as the expansion of new competitors abroad, has actually added a strategic dimension of external support to the precarious risk structures all these behemoths carry.

Globalization has indeed ripped the sails of many of Japan's proud export manufacturers. "Foreign markets [today] provide extraordinary stimulus," observes Samuel Armacost, International Advisor to Toshiba and Chairman of Stanford Research Institute. "You can't control the competitive environment like you can in your domestic marketplace . . . I think the lack of a competitive response of a number of Japanese corporate names that were formidable competitors a decade ago is because they have not responded to external stimulus."

Toshiba has responded, is responding, and will go on with more response. And that, to the reader's good fortune, is the frame into which we fit this portrait of Toshiba, at this age: a company saying farewell to whatever safe harbor "Japan, Inc." once afforded, swept up in the challenge of yet another tidal wave of change, visibly and openly working hard and fast as it can to transform itself to meet the markets as they are, head-on.

A company enjoying the challenge? No, not with still so much at stake and all the crucial transitions still in progress (especially amidst the economic turmoil of the early 2000s).

A company in danger? Not quite yet. But one not quite yet safely through the storm and secure in its course on the new sea of global business, either.

★

The reader is ushered in right here, then, ringside to the story of Toshiba: a world heavyweight champion halfway through the fight, stung by many swift and hard blows but rising and ready for the bell and bouts to come.

Confident of winning by technological knockout.

The Ten In-house Companies of Toshiba Corporation
(Each company has its own company president)

iValue Creation Company
(see Chapter 8)
Social Infrastructure Systems Company
(see Chapter 5)
Mobile Communications Company
(see Chapter 9)
Semiconductor Company
(see Chapter 11)
Medical Systems Company
(see Chapter 20)
e-Solutions Company
(see Chapter 19)
Digital Media Network Company
(see Chapter 18)
Power Systems & Services Company
(see Chapter 6)
Display Devices & Components Company
(see Chapter 12)
Home Appliances Company
(see Chapter 4)

NOTES

1. *Kodansha Encyclopedia of Japan*, Kodansha Ltd., Tokyo, 1983
2. *Japan Company Handbook*, First Section, Toyo Keizai Inc., Tokyo, Autumn 2001
3. Martin Fransman, *Japan's Computer and Communications Industry: The Evolution of Industrial Giants and Global Competitiveness*, Oxford University Press, Oxford and New York, 1995

CHAPTER TWO
MAPMAKER

Taizo Nishimuro sorted carefully through his worries. There were plenty. It was 1996 and he had just been, very unexpectedly, boosted over eight other candidates into the presidency of Toshiba. Adding up all the factors to plan where he should lead his group of 189,000, he quickly hit the wall of a tough conclusion: "If Toshiba stays as it is, there is no future for this company."

No scale could measure the shock of the tremors Nishimuro's decision and his redirections would set loose in a 121-year-old, mossback behemoth like Toshiba. Thirty-four members of the board, 15 business divisions, more than 800 affiliates scattered around the world: a literally electric beacon of Japanese business aristocracy, custom, punctilio, and venerability.

All headed, in one hellacious hurry, for the dinosaurs' bone yard.

An almost classical inference, really, perhaps one even shrewdly desired by the executives who installed the 61-year-old Nishimuro at Toshiba's pinnacle just then. In a corporate hierarchy dominated for decades by electrical men – men who knew, understood, and counted out year upon year of dividends on the solid steel and brass and copper shells of dynamos, generators, and locomotives – all tradition was displaced by a single marketing executive whose specialties were semiconductors and optical media, and who had spent more than a quarter of his career in – America! Unthinkable.

But that's what Nishimuro thought in 1996, the unthinkable.

Because as he had watched the rising dominance of Silicon Valley and of South Korea, of computers and digital communications stretching out around the world, from his post as vice-chairman of Toshiba America in the early 1990s, he had understood what was unfolding: globalization, and the internets of new industries upon which it traveled.

Since those years, he had known that Toshiba was missing it, and stood in increasing danger. "Toshiba is one of the typical Japanese industries that has to realize that danger, and has to initiate the changes which are necessary to survive." Five years later, Nishimuro sits relaxed in an armchair of his chairman's suite at Toshiba Corp. – and the verb tense he uses most is the present. "When I found myself president, I knew I had to declare that we must make these changes."

The changes made headlines worldwide. "Looking back on what Toshiba was, from that standpoint – from the mixture of IT business growth and globalization – the company just looked very Japanese. Caught halfway between traditional Japanese business style and globalization. We have to get all the way over to globalization or there might not be a future for Toshiba."

Moving swiftly, Nishimuro:

- Began cleaving away whole product sectors – automatic teller machines, automobile headlamps, home air conditioners – by selling them outright, or joint-venturing them with other partners, to either liquidate Toshiba's losing businesses or strengthen them to greater profitability through restrategizing the entire approach.
- Cut Toshiba's main business groups from 15 to 8 (presently ten), along sharply defined business lines to, first, get as close as possible an alignment between Toshiba's experts and their customers, and, second, to free their leadership up from the bureaucratic morass of the dense corporate headquarters structure.

- Brought in the executive-officer system for the leadership of these ten operations, making them all separate "in-house" companies and making their officers and mid-level managers directly responsible for performance, so both could be judged on profit and loss results every year.
- Reduced the board of directors from 34 to 12 (presently 13), tearing down a whole arras of ceremonial court pageantry and focusing the management (all 34 board members were salaried Toshiba executives) on managing every minute, getting the products out and the profits in.
- Set new and startlingly high goals for corporate return-on-equity and shareholder value, the better to attract capital from investors around the world.

Nishimuro reassured his managers that everybody would remain on the Toshiba team, though they would be wearing different uniforms. And he titillated the business journalists by insisting that Toshiba must abandon old-style, dark-suit Japanese bureaucratic direction and adopt international management orientations, dumping losing or break-even businesses wherever identified to refocus stagnant corporate assets, and asking always, always, what businesses should Toshiba really be in?

To help answer that question, or at least plot a strategy for researching it, he brought in a team of outside consultants to help him with a total, 12-month review of the whole company. When they left, the reforms began. All of Japanese business, it is not too much to say, has been watching for five years to see what the outcome would be.

Taizo Nishimuro is a tall, cosmopolitan, and erudite man with a deep voice, elegantly inflected, who was raised by a strict father to read Confucian analects every morning from the age of five. "I close my eyes and I can still see them, the lines of ancient Chinese characters. And one motto I have taken from Confucius:

'When you find your mistake,' it goes, 'you must never hesitate to mend it.' That's quite strong, really, because first you have to be smart enough to find it, and second you have to have the courage to make the change."

What he had done years before, as the elected student-body president of his elite alma mater, Keio University, required smarts and courage in equal measure when the pro-Communist *Zengakuren* student movement threatened to take it over and make a springboard of it for leftist agitation.

"I was against letting them in, and we were the largest student organization not to fall into affiliation with them at the time. That gave me great experience in how to cope with people who are aggressive and also politically biased."

It took more courage, plus the will to study harder, when Nishimuro unexpectedly earned a one-year scholarship to the University of British Columbia. Without even enough cash to buy a plane ticket, he headed for the docks of Shibaura – ironically just a few meters from where his corporate headquarters stand today – and booked a freighter for Vancouver.

When he was picked up at the docks there by a Canadian student, he realized he could understand no more than ten per cent of what he heard. "It wasn't a problem with accent. It was that my English was so poor." After two months of Olympian, all-night effort, he began to make sense of the classroom lectures, and topped off his academic year with some postgraduate study of a special kind: he worked two months in a Canadian sawmill. "And then my English really improved!"

Though Nishimuro still dresses in the usual dark, subdued hues of the Japanese executive suit, he does so with a tailored meticulousness that evinces both his even disposition and effective, straight-on brand of communication. He is said never to have demonstrated anger, among colleagues or competitors.

Perhaps he has learned a different way to manage adversity:

35 years ago he was diagnosed with a degenerative muscular disease that was expected to be fatal. Treatment undertaken at an American hospital halted its course, but left him with a crippled leg and to this day he has a pronounced limp that necessitates the use of a cane. Normally, Japanese corporations count disabilities a reason to keep a manager from such a high post. But to speak to him – to walk with him – at the helm of Toshiba today, one would notice little more than his vibrant personal and physical energy.

Now, having left the Toshiba presidency in 2000 to take the chairman's post, he spends a deal of his time representing his business and his industry as vice-chairman of Keidanren, the Japan Federation of Economic Organizations (almost, as commentators have it, the "Vatican" of Japanese big business), and as new chairman of the Japan–US Business Council. In the summer of 2001, he was the lone Japanese business executive invited to an American Enterprise Institute private seminar in Colorado, where he exchanged views with US Vice President Dick Cheney, Federal Reserve Chairman Alan Greenspan, and prominent members of the White House staff, US government agencies, and businesses and academia.

But he keeps a very close eye, together with now–president Tadashi Okamura, on the company and how it fares under the regime of change he instituted.

The answers are still pending. As Nishimuro moved up to his present job the corporation, along with all of the IT industry around the world, began to fall into the deep, darkening pit of looming global recession. The lesson underscored this time was that if globalism can bring universal opportunity, it can also bring universal misery.

Toshiba in 2002 will fall from profit to loss, big loss. Thus in the first area, divestiture and reorganization of businesses for higher profit, the pressures have quickened and the final response is unknowable. Already in 2001 it had been announced that semiconductor commodity DRAMs, a horrible loss-maker, would be sold to Micron Technology of the United States. Liquid crystal display screens, for portable computers, cell phones, and the like, would be turned into a co-venture with Matsushita Electric Industrial.

Television-set manufacture, merely a break-even business for Toshiba in today's hot competition with Asian firms, has seen all production for the Japanese market and for China moved to China.

Still the blood was dripping from the ledgers in the spring of 2002, and critics were derisive of both the slowness and the reluctance with which Toshiba was getting out from under losing operations.

Yet how much more loss would be booked on assets, Nishimuro had to consider, if Toshiba simply closed down factories or spun off or dumped companies at fire-sale prices to satisfy the critics? A little of each was still being forced on the firm at the end of 2001, but only in line with the planned metrics of overall corporate restructuring – not in panic.

And the strategic success of the new in-house businesses structure? "To my eyes, and to Okamura-san's eyes, the speed [of change inside the new companies] is not fast enough . . . There are people, it is very natural, that try to keep the old traditional way. All those initiatives that I had begun were delayed by a year of this need for consensus-building. But it was necessary time. I had to keep the team together, and they need anywhere from months to a year to be convinced the change is necessary."

The abbreviation of the board has helped the effectiveness of management, Nishimuro feels. "I appointed some new statutory auditors to check on what we were doing right and wrong. One was a retired Supreme Court judge. At first he just sat quietly and listened to the meetings. After about the third session, he told me it was interesting – but so many of the topics appeared to have been decided in advance, and then to have been introduced merely for automatic approval. And he said, this is against the commercial law! He was very influential in making our new, smaller board meetings very active: we stopped the automatic approvals, and began to really discuss things in depth."

Nishimuro's tack to try to introduce creative, innovative management dynamism, in a setting where modern business metrics will mercilessly measure every success and failure and the careers of hundreds will swing in the balance, is not meant to be draconian. His in-house companies, of course, are something of a managerial ruse for the present: they are fully held, recognized as parts of Toshiba Corporation, and will only operate as independently as Toshiba lets them. The present "valuation level" of any decisions allowed to them without necessity for a corporate OK is five billion yen, about 42 million dollars.

In-house companies are not a new concept in corporate management, of course, even in Japan. But for a corps of high-ranked management lacking a new and clear conceptualization of the huge and dangerous challenges facing it, it may be the best form of "instant MBA" Toshiba can come up with.

"We will have two real goals in our assessments of their results. One is to sharpen the productiveness of our real core businesses, of course. The other is future-oriented, to find out which of them will serve as incubators for the technologies and business of the future." Nishimuro's real dream for Toshiba is to find, define, and storm the market with highly advanced or at least highly desirable and highly profitable benchmark products of Toshiba's own, like Canon's laser printer, Sony's CD format for music – and Toshiba's DVD. That's what the "incubators" are for.

But it still means some in-house companies will be judged on profits, while others will be judged on the promise of profits.

"It's true, this is a bit of a gamble. But without [both] those ambitions, our people would not be energized. Now we need the people who aim to grow with us. And for that, we need dream targets for them to achieve."

CHAPTER THREE
LESSONS LEARNED

Tadashi Okamura learned his best lessons about running a business the hardest way, from bitter experience. His first management assignment was to sell Toshiba's new machinery-control systems to Japanese plant operators. "Our strategy was to make the same kind of systems as our best competitors. But since our competitors already had the best systems, no one would even look at ours."

Ten long years went by, before microprocessors came on the scene. "We decided to develop a control system using them – the first such system in Japan. The other people who all made analog systems did not want to change, and we had a tough time selling against them still. But eventually, the factory people understood how much better our system was, and they gave us their input as to what they really wanted the systems to do. We developed solutions – and we became a success. That product line still sells well."

First lesson learned: it's no good to copy the market leader. Get there first.

Second lesson: To be first, you first have to have the most advanced technology.

Third lesson: To make what sells, listen to what the customer really wants.

Fourth lesson: It may take years to win a market with a product made in just one.

Those lessons still define Toshiba, and the 63-year-old Okamura, president since June 2000, interprets, reinterprets, and where necessary reconstructs the new managerial plans first unfolded by Chairman Nishimuro, to redefine them in third-millennium business terms for his senior and mid-level executives:

- Use your best competitors, and their best products, as bench-marks to exceed what they offer.
- Pay attention to the technological resources available through-out this mammoth enterprise, to improve your products and to give yourself the market edge.
- Use technology to give customers exactly what they want, not what you think they should want. Listen, listen, listen to their voices.
- And plan and invest for a future you cannot even see today, for it will be here, with all its opportunities, soon enough.

Okamura does not rest on pontification. On any given day, all of his managers and white-collar employees might come to their desks to find a computer e-mail (there are over 86,000 computers in use inside Toshiba, more than two for each such staffer) sent directly from the president. "We call it push mail, and I send it to everyone whenever there is important news for the company. Each one of them can respond directly to me, if he or she chooses."

There's also the enterprise's e-newspaper, for all its employees. And each month, on a Saturday, Okamura gathers a group of about a hundred of his key general managers, each time from a different business sector, and spends the day giving and listening to management reports. On the evenings of those days he drinks a little beer with all of them, listening to opinions.

And of course, there is the unending stream of plant visits, and tours of sales units and subsidiaries, and . . .

And any number of other activities indispensable to the role of evangelist that the president must play to his own company, to complete the switch in its thinking from stolid, craftsman-like manufacturing excellence to serving new people in new markets in new places with new needs, in a hurry – without losing the production quality.

To put it simply, he has to get his vast organization to understand they now live in a new world, where the concept of information technology embraces far more than just personal computers. An office world in which, he told a journalist in the fall of 2000, computers are still the core. "But when people are on the street, they now use mobile terminals [instead], mainly cellular phones. And at home, [digital] TV sets will be the center of IT."[1]

All of these separate technologies are blending together, intertwining, while serving markets that must be conceptualized separately to understand the exact needs and potentials of each. Okamura sees the three pillars of Toshiba's business from now as three distinct domains, he tells his people: industry and society, the individual, and components of high technology.

Then he comes home and sits at his desk, where the job awaits of figuring out how they can all be reasonably tied in under the brutal cyclicality of markets for each of them: for products such as semiconductor memories cratering around the earth; such as civil works projects under declining public budgets; such as cell phones that aren't selling in a world running over with capacity and sliding into recession.

To balance all of this on the high-wire of a 188,000-staff company, "We have defined three winning models for our business strategies," says Okamura. "One is the innovator type," where the company invents and fields epoch-making new products with excellent margins.

"The second one we call the integrator model," where Toshiba's strong core of competencies and patents can be used in partnership with other firms, both allies from different markets and competitors from Toshiba's own neighborhoods – or more likely, both. "The product will be a value-added integration." (We shall see many samples of these integrations below.)

"And the third pattern will be a platform-type winning model." In this scenario, Toshiba furnishes, under proprietary contract or on the open market, its high-quality manufactures for any industrial customer to buy and use as components in anything it wants – even in such things as portable computers which compete directly with Toshiba's own.

It sounds ambitious, tactical and well-reasoned, the sort of insight one might expect from a tall, fit, and almost bullishly built executive like Okamura, who played the tough game of rugby for his university and Toshiba's corporate team and who hasn't added a single extra pound to his waistline since. The energy he displays seems more than adequate for the challenges and strategies so openly enumerated.

The problem, as critics never fail to point out, is that for Toshiba, none of it is innovative at all. In form, it's been standard business practice around this company for years. What's new? What's really going to make it a different and better and more profitable path for Toshiba now, they demand to know.

"I think we have to definitely speed things up," says the president. "And I believe that [ingraining these principles at every level] is a kind of now-or-never opportunity."

One of Tadashi Okamura's favorite pastimes is motoring. While he was studying for his MBA at the University of Wisconsin in the early 1970s, Okamura suddenly decided to pack his wife and two-year-old daughter into his car and set out for Mexico. An uncle of his, a doctor, through a series of events almost scripted in Hollywood, had many years before interrupted a journey to Mexico City to save the life of a gravely ill small girl in a seaside village, had stayed on as the local doctor, had married – and Okamura's family in Mexico had grown to about 60 people he'd never met.

"I drove 600 kilometers a day. It was really a thrill to drive through the mountains of bandits at midnight. I could have been so adventurous because I was young."[2]

He's no longer that young, but the Toshiba president must feel a little bit of the same kind of thrill when he ventures abroad these days to explain what's going on in his company to shareholders' and securities analysts' meetings.

"Until last year what everybody has been telling me is that the company must be able to define itself, and get out of this role of the company who does everything. This year, I could see a change in their attitude. About one-third of the institutional investors told me that our future challenge would not be as they had said last year, to have more focus, but more to have good synergy between our three areas of activities [consumer, social infrastructure, and high-tech industry]."

So what's a chief executive officer to think?

"I think it's based on the fact that more and more people acknowledge the IT revolution actually was about the convergence between the virtual economy and the real economy. And so this year, it's OK to rethink in my terms of Toshiba as being able to show strengths in conversions and synergies."

It's not simply an argument over whether Toshiba has been right all along. Okamura knows well enough that success lies in getting his company to do what it already does, just in very different ways. Because the customers are not just Japanese anymore, but arced like a rainbow across the whole earthly horizon, and because that means that the technologies do not drive the society the way they once did.

"It's understandable that people may question why we are all of a sudden pushing this old slogan of Voice of the Customers, that the customer comes first. But we have to be able to reflect as never before in our development of products and services the needs of our customers. Otherwise we cannot satisfy them anymore, and we cannot just go on being a technology-driven company."

What Okamura really is trying to do, this means, is transform a conservative, production-oriented, old-line Japanese enterprise (a "gearhead culture," as one Western magazine described the firm[3]) into one that has primarily a service company's values. The "service" here is to design, make, and deliver the specific, almost custom-made thing that the individual consumer wants to buy at the moment.

Nor is it a matter of touchy-feely ego redirection. "Globalization's effects will be more and more fierce in our business. We have to redistribute the production base [to economize in the labor market, as well as to get closer to the customer]. Whether it is in China, in Southeast Asia, in the Middle East, wherever – we feel we have to be even more present wherever there is a market potential."

So like a fine, old, hand-built sailing ship, Toshiba unties from the wharf of the Japanese "managed economy" that the world is passing by, and heads out into deep blue waters spanning the globe, to follow "a grand design, or a big scheme with a long-term vision, to see very clearly where you want to go from the beginning, the strategy for getting there, and to see what kind of products should go where in this new global market."

NOTES

1. "Toshiba transforms for IT revolution," *Japan Times*, Tokyo, 12 June 2001
2. "Profile of Tadashi Okamura, Toshiba President," *Nikkan Gendai*, Tokyo, 10 January 2001
3. "Toshiba: A Giant Struggles to Reinvent Itself," *Business Week* Asian Edition, New York, 13 October 1997

PART TWO

THE TAIZO ISHIZAKA ERA
(1949–1957)

The man before them was in every way extraordinary. A former president of one of Japan's largest insurance firms, then a president of one of Japan's largest electrical manufacturers, he was now in his twelfth year of the chairmanship of Keidanren – Japan's Federation of Economic Organizations – and as such the "Pope" of Japanese enterprise. He looked so familiar in that chair, heading today's general meeting, that it seemed almost unbelievable when he closed the agenda by rising to announce that, at the age of 82, he was retiring, effective at once.

But the rows of executives, in shock, were unwilling for him to go that day without at least a few words summarizing this most protean of postwar executive careers. Obliging, Ishizaka rose and began slowly. "If my mother were still alive and could see me here today, saying goodbye after a full dozen years as chairman of Keidanren, well, she would have just said, 'Oh, that sly little boy Taizo!'"

Taizo Ishizaka started to say more. But his voice broke suddenly, and he just sat down, unable to go on. As the room dissolved from stock-stillness into a wave of wild applause, there was the undeniable sense of an age passing.

Though he was a sensitive person for a kingmaker, and perforce a diplomat in the delicate job of aligning Japan's postwar economic reconstruction, there was nothing aristocratic in the background of Toshiba's first giant leader of the postwar age. He was born on a farm in Saitama.

His father hated farm work, so he just left the land and went up to Tokyo with his family. "They were all very poor," says Shunsuke Miyao, now retired from Toshiba but Ishizaka's secretary for the last 13 years of his life, and editor of the Ishizaka diaries.

"So the father started out as something like a clerk in a courthouse, and they had many children. The parents had a hard time raising them all. So Taizo certainly did not come from wealth."

But he got an education – a good one – and by the war years worked his way up to the presidency of the Dai-Ichi Life Insurance Co. As Dai-Ichi was one of the biggest shareholders in Toshiba (it still owns 3.7% of the company today), he was chosen for a Toshiba board member even before the end of the war. When defeat came, he was purged by the Occupation government.

But Ishizaka was not idle for long. Across town Toshiba was not recovering, but sinking further into chaos. Kiichiro Sato, the president of Mitsui Bank, Toshiba's main financial support, asked Ishizaka to take over the mess. It was 1949. He was already 63. Toshiba's problems were bad labor troubles, and "I think," says Miyao, "he thought it all over very, very carefully, discussing it with many people. But in the end he decided to take it."

Ishizaka, with the proper endorsements, asked for special permission from the occupation authorities to be de-purged for just this purpose, and suddenly he was in charge.

Toshiba was already huge, a manufacturer of everything from light bulbs to locomotives to enormous electrical generators. At demobilization it had more than 100 factories in Japan, and others in Shanghai and elsewhere in China and in Korea. The staffing was more than 100,000 regular workers, unpayable in the disaster of the immediate days of defeat. The crippled nation, under the

American government, was soon the backdrop against which freed political prisoners, many of them Marxists or Communists, were soon waging a struggle for union control of companies. "Toshiba was chosen [for a union action target] because it had a network already all over Japan, and because it was an older company compared to other industrial companies. The communist party thought that by infiltrating members of the communist movement inside Toshiba unions, they could invade Japan very easily through the Toshiba network," is Miyao's succinct analysis.

Strikes and other labor actions were shaking the struggling company everywhere. Relations between Toshiba and its unions were openly combative. Negotiations over restructuring, wages, and a seeming thousand other causes the unions claimed to have were interminable and insufferable: over ten hours at a stretch some days, the company claimed, without even an allowance for management members to visit the restrooms or take meals. "And even," says Miyao, recounting tales of the time, "labor negotiators who reached over to stub out their live cigarettes on the president's head."

Ishizaka stepped in, and first "created several proposals. He had a very clear vision and policies which he laid open to the unions. In his diary, he summarized them in four phases: first was restructuring the organization and labor roster, second was to reform the structure of the company's leadership, expelling incapable executives, third was to do a funding plan with clear accounting – and fourth, to negotiate with General Electric for technical support. It was with the clarity of his plans that things began to simmer down in the union–management confrontation. Employment was eventually reduced by 20 per cent, after a lot more fighting with the union."

Getting Toshiba back on an even keel organizationally was

important – but arguably much of the company's survival, as Japan's own, was due to the outbreak of the Korean War, and the huge procurement orders from the American government which restarted all of the Japanese industrial economy.

Probably what Ishizaka did that was most important to prepare for Toshiba's future was his inauguration of a policy of business alliances, with friends and competitors alike, that has grown in importance and influence in Toshiba down to the present – in fact to the point of being again what it was in those early days: a key survival strategy. What got that strategy launched, there is little doubt, was the overall effort of Japanese manufacturers to import American technology and process wherever and whenever they could.

But "Alliances had to be made with other [domestic] companies," says Miyao. "And he had a large influence over the entire industry. And on the other hand he tried very hard to negotiate with the foreign leading companies, like General Electric, RCA, Westinghouse, and so on, to introduce their top-level technologies."

Toshiba's first big job was reestablishing and extending the crumpled network of national electrification. "It was important to tie up with GE, which was in the forefront of technology for larger-capacity generators. And then, electronics: a very early start back then. President Ishizaka was often going to the US to lay out the future technology for electronics. He spoke English, German, and even French, all well enough to converse freely in those languages. He was very independent and in a way individualistic.

"President Ishizaka was a man interested in anything. He had great curiosity. He was a big man physically, but also in terms of thinking he was big – he thought big. He was always interested in people. He always wanted to know everyone's full name – their first name as well as their last. He wanted to establish a personal relationship with anyone he met. For example if someone told him 'Toyota says this or that,' he always wanted to know right away '*Who* in Toyota? Who said it?' And depending on who it was, he would judge whether the information was reliable or not.

"He had also a fine, clear memory – personalities and names stayed with him for years. He enjoyed talking with people and when the topic was interesting, he was not so quiet. He played both golf and *Go* [a Japanese board game], and he was a painter – oils, watercolors, ink, etc. He would copy out in calligraphy from Confucius and others of the sages and famous penmen. He made pottery, even. He helped organize contributions for research programs at Stanford Research Institute, in California.

"But most important, I think, was that his guiding principle as a business executive was free competition. He was thinking of the companies not so much in relation to the country or the government, but only as one of the nuclei in the atoms of a highly competitive world. And it was this competition, he believed, that would drive technological innovation, to contribute to society at large.

"Nowadays, anybody would tell you that – but in the 1960s, as Japan had to consider entering the world of free trade and free capitalism, most of the other industries' top executives were against it. But Ishizaka as the chairman of Keidanren pushed for that openness very hard, because he thought that was very important for the future of Japan and because he was so powerful nobody dared to stand against him."

Obviously, many did stand against Ishizaka, and the ultimate survival and prosperity of his own company down to the twenty-first century has been due in no small measure to government protection from external competitors, regulation of domestic competition, direct subsidy, and mercantilist foreign policy.

It was in the era of Ishizaka's leadership, though, when it was the "legacy businesses" of Toshiba, working mostly on the strength of their own long experience and their own understanding of technologies, players, and customers in their markets, that brought in the money which stabilized the foundation on which Toshiba stands today.

CHAPTER FOUR
TAKE IT TO THE HOUSE

It was 1955 when Toshiba brought out its *Jido Denki-gama*, automatic electric rice cooker, and Makoto Nakagawa, now the company president of Toshiba's Home Appliances Company, was just a skinny kid in the third year of middle school out in the sticks of Fukui Prefecture. It wasn't until three or four years later, the first time he came up to visit Tokyo, that he actually saw one of the marvelous machines.

Now, stepping out of his car and sampling the air like a connoisseur along the busy main boulevard of Akihabara (the world-renowned wonderland of discount electronics stores in downtown Tokyo, where Japan's leading electrical and electronics firms first unveil their newest and best products), he knows every last detail about every last home appliance made or sold in Japan, intimately. It's his job.

"Our aim is to make marketing our competence," says Nakagawa, stepping smartly through the door of a huge, multistory appliance discounter in the heart of Akihabara. He is about to improve his aim.

"So I don't waste time in a lot of meetings back in the headquarters building. I think 15 minutes is enough for a discussion about anything, don't you? After that, I want to be out here, watching the customers, finding out what I'm selling and what I should be selling to meet customer demand better. This," he says, shaking the hand of the bowing floor manager of chain appliance-seller Onoden's flagship retail store who has rushed out to greet him, "is Mister Yamada, my marketing teacher."

Home Appliances is one of those honored "legacy businesses" that has come down to today's Toshiba through its long, manically active past. Long before it was Toshiba, the ancestral company Hakunetsu-sha produced Japan's first electric incandescent lamp, in 1890 (it still makes them: each year, Toshiba turns out millions of bulbs of every description). The nation's first electric fan was introduced in 1894. In 1930 "we made the country's first electric refrigerator," says Toshiaki Suzuki, from the company's General Planning Division. "It had a 120-liter capacity and in those days, it cost as much as a new house."

Today Toshiba refrigerators dominate Japan's 10 billion-dollar white goods appliance industry, placing at the top with a 20% share, almost a million units sold every year. The brand is also No. 1 in vacuum cleaners and irons; either No. 1 or No. 2, depending on the year, in washing machines; and second in microwave ovens.

Yet in this market, as densely packed with competitive products as the store in which Nakagawa stands, that's not good enough. Appliances account for 10% of Toshiba's annual sales – but profit margins are extremely thin. "We've had a tough decade," says Nakagawa. "Japan has had a tough decade. But what I tell my people is that it's because we were unable to change or adapt fast enough to match the speed of our customers' lifestyle changes.

"That's why I'm here." He means not only here in his current position, but here in Akihabara. "I tell them now that they must all be so close to the customers that they can feel them breathing. Because all our products live, 365 days a year, side by side with our customers – inside their lives."

Nakagawa visits retailers constantly, on his lunch breaks, on his business trips. He makes his engineers and his product planners spend whole weekends inside these big stores, all over the country, just watching customers, noting what sells and what doesn't sell. They send Internet reports back to the company constantly, so the marketing staff knows which store is stocking what, what colors are popular, where the biggest discounts are being given.

Right now Nakagawa is looking into the surgically sparkling interior of Toshiba's biggest refrigerator, as Onoden's Yamada briefs him on how the machine is doing with the customers. "It seems we've already won the game," says Yamada. "Summer's here early, and the forecasts are for hot weather all the way into September. Refrigerators have already started selling well."

"I always listen to this kind of talk," says Nakagawa, "to guess when will be the peak season each year for a product, and decide how we should control production and supply." Does that mean it's such a sensitive business that production schedules have to be decided week by week for the whole country? "You can't know how to get the real competitive advantage unless you stand this close to the customer," he says, turning back to Yamada to discuss color selections. "Well, it might help if Toshiba had a few more color choices," suggests the discounter discreetly.

Nakagawa explains his own idea: let the customers pick whatever color they want from a sample catalog, and Toshiba will deliver their choice to their home in two days.

The home appliance market, in a society where almost 14% of all households are composed of people older than 65, is impossibly mature, and sales of both refrigerators and washing machines in Japan have fallen by 5% over the past five years.[1]

Despite Toshiba's achievement of a steady 1% rise in home-market share per year, the appliance retail sector has over the past decade robbed the manufacturers of virtually all pricing control. Huge discount "big-box" appliance stores, organized in chains that buy as many as tens of thousands of refrigerators or washers a year, blanket the land and now make 80% of all appliance sales in the country.

This leaves Toshiba facing either grueling, grind-the-enemy-down price wars (and the enemy now includes a growing flood of Korean and Chinese bargain-priced knock-offs of Japanese appliances) – or go constantly to the technology drawing board, to build in value-added on every sale.

Japanese customers are very pampered now, and the widespread introduction of the credit card – instant consumer loans – has meant they can justify the purchase of new, luxury features by stretching payments out over the coming years.

That is why Nakagawa's refrigerators look very little like, for example, American ones. His best model has five, not just two, compartment drawers, where a second motor built into the box can vary temperatures in the compartments from cool fresh air, for produce, to an exact one degree above zero centigrade, for keeping *sashimi* fish fresh enough to eat raw after a week. Another setting moves another compartment to minus 18 centigrade, the perfect temperature for quickly chilling beer when the gang shows up unexpectedly.

"We'll have to fight hard in the middle-level market, where price counts, that's certain," he says, admitting that not everyone with a credit card or without one will splurge for the big, value-added luxury features. "Here, we're going to depend on IT manufacturing, new technologies, and perhaps even overseas production of our own to remain competitive."

Perhaps indeed: Toshiba had already in 2000 commissioned production of some refrigerators and washing machines to companies in China.[2]

One by one, in fact, Nakagawa's big Japanese competitors are becoming two-by-two ventures and alliances, to pool risk and investment in the ever-tighter market: Sharp has tied up with Sanyo, Matsushita and Hitachi. And Toshiba itself has signed with Samsung of Korea to develop and produce washer-dryers.[3] But that isn't all. Ever mindful of those fat margins in the high end of the market, Toshiba has also signed a "comprehensive alliance" agreement with famed European appliance maker AB Electrolux of Sweden. Not only will they share technologies and parts procurement to cut costs, but Toshiba already markets a special appliance marque "Electrolux by Toshiba," produced in Thailand and elsewhere and imported to Japan.

That's, as you might expect with a shrewd manager like Nakagawa, hardly the end of it. Home-appliance engineers are working with the Bluetooth and wireless technologies of short-range communication links, to adapt them to controlling ovens and other appliances for integrated kitchen systems. Electrolux, Nakagawa points out, "is already making those next-generation kinds of model homes where if you want a certain something for dinner, you can prepare everything, timed to your arrival at your dinner table, with a computer."

Toshiba of course makes computers, wireless communications technologies, servers, and appliances for the kitchen and home such as microwave ovens and air conditioners. Does the combination, or at least the potential combination, suggest anything to industry watchers?

It ought to. By 2002, one of Nakagawa's product-development engineers said, Toshiba will have put on the market both a refrigerator and a microwave oven that are wired to receive commands from a household server, when it is introduced "in the future."

"I started to play rugby, you know, when I was 40 years old," says Nakagawa, who sometimes on overseas business trips makes his calls (and visits the local appliance markets, of course) by day and sleeps not in hotels, but on jetliners. "I learned the importance of teamwork, and I learned that once you put your game strategy into place, you must never give it up. It's the only way to win. As managers, we must not make mistakes in this game. And we have to stick to our own plan, of always building for our customers the vision of a Toshiba lifestyle.

"But we also," he grins, waving goodbye to his Akihabara "teacher" and heading back to the office to tell his engineers what he learned, "have to enjoy business as a game. We need to enjoy taking the risks."

NOTES

1. "Competition forces rivals into tie-up," *Asahi Evening News*, Tokyo, 4 July 2001
2. "Japan appliance makers take big-ticket gamble," *Nikkei Weekly*, Tokyo, 30 July 2001
3. "Toshiba, Samsung to develop washer-dryers," Kyodo News reported on the *Japan Today* website, Tokyo, 31 August 2001

CHAPTER FIVE
WHATEVER IT TAKES

You can make a young boy happy, any father knows, by giving him a toy train set.

But you can overjoy Toshiba Corp. by presenting it, together with six corporate allies, with a contract for an entire 300-km-per-hour passenger train system – trains, tracks, signals, controllers, everything down to the crossing gates. Because Toshiba's been waiting, and building the know-how, for a job like this for 102 years.

Toshiba built the motors for Japan's first electric railway in 1901. Ever since, design and construction of railways and similar systems – trolleys, electrical buses, specialized long- and short-haul freight locomotives – have been specialist knowledge of the company, one of its legacy businesses that helped build Japan's industrial infrastructure from the ground up.

The present-day Social Infrastructure Systems Company, 6,600 employees strong, has a much wider range of products than that: it specializes also in water-supply and water-treatment systems, large-scale electrical machinery installations, and on and on – as we shall see in a moment.

But the new railroad package, signed in December 2000, is especially important to Toshiba because aside from representing one of its largest ever export contracts (nearly 3 billion dollars in eventual sales, and perhaps more), it is the first major, full-scale engineering job the in-house company has landed *abroad*. Toshiba's management is intensely interested in expanding its classic strengths in the legacy businesses to snare more contracts in the global market, and the Taiwan Railroad job shows how it can be done.

Social Infrastructure Systems, despite its size (about 3.5 billion dollars in sales annually), has been until now the second most domestically oriented part of all of Toshiba. That's because much of its work is done in civil-engineering projects, and so about two-thirds of its income has derived from business with various departments of national and local government in Japan.

That business is so massive in scope and scale it includes whole divisions for handling:

- Transportation Systems – railroads and parts
- Aerospace and Electronics Systems – from radar installations to space satellites
- Power Electronics Systems – for management of automated manufacturing plants, etc.
- Control and Measurement Systems
- Public and Industrial Systems – for energy, water, waste treatment, and other services
- International Operations – Systems and Solutions Division – for manufacturing plants, broadcast systems, and airports
- Toshiba-GE Automation Venture – making control systems for paper-mill machinery, steel plants, etc.

The new railroad, to be built in Taiwan between the major port city of Kaohsiung and the capital Taipei, will reduce travel time from the present four and a half hours by regular train to 90 minutes by Bullet express. The project marks a new age not just for big Toshiba international sales, but also for the emergence of technical integrations that make planning, building, and supplying a railroad almost as sophisticated as preparing a regional civil aviation system.

"Under the Transportation System Division's roof now comes *everything* that relates to a railroad," says Takatsugu Yamaya, Social

Infrastructure Systems' Project Manager. "Motor systems, computer systems, automated ticket gates and ticket sales machines, telecommunications links, electrical subsystems for the cars such as power supply wiring to motors and air conditioners and lights, operations management systems, radio control systems, rolling simulator systems, and on and on: all these we either are supplying or will supply."

Toshiba landed its contract by joining a seven-firm Japanese venture group, including four of the big general trading firms unique to Japan and known as *sogo shosha*, plus Mitsubishi Heavy Industries and Kawasaki Heavy Industries.

The type of contract Toshiba and the others negotiated is called Build-Operate-Transfer, which is becoming a standard means of sharing risk when such mammoth industrial projects are first framed. The Japan consortium members have agreed to invest with the Taiwanese prime project organizer, Taiwan High Speed Rail Corp., 394 million dollars for a ten per cent ownership stake in the railroad itself.

When the 345-km line is put into service in 2006, the partners will operate it together, making a profit not only from the sales of equipment for construction and manufacture, but from stock dividends and the eventual sale of the shares.

"And then," says Yamaya, "we have maintenance and servicing contracts as well for all the equipment we sell. And we can expect a lot more related sales to develop as we go along regarding [more] tracks, equipment management systems, local transportation serving each station, and even redevelopment of station-front properties." The railroad's master development plan calls for eleven new stations to be installed along the line, meaning there should be new suburban neighborhoods sprouting outward from each. "All of this should mean future business opportunities for Toshiba."

Future opportunity is something Social Infrastructure Systems

Co. will likely need. As noted, the vast majority of its contracts come from Japan's government projects. At the start of this century, though, the nation's finances called for a paring-down of public outlays, and it began to look very much like government contracting was about to slow for the long term.

"The figure for the government's percentage of our total business," says Kiichiro Ito, Senior Manager of the Business Strategy and Planning Dept., "is slowly falling already, by about five per cent per year."

Ito acknowledges that two crucial changes must be effected within his company as soon as possible. One is the entry into more consortia, for the type of overseas work that the Taiwan Railroad represents, and the other is the transposition of Social Infrastructure Service products, from off-the-shelf machines and parts that need only meet routine government specifications, into solution-oriented systems that take into account the Voice of the Customer, and the problems the customer is actually trying to solve.

"We can't go on just selling our clients some equipment and saying goodbye. We have to see where we can add value for him. Perhaps we have to take a stake, by agreeing on receiving payments from future revenues earned by our systems. If necessary, we must not only build it, but just like the railroad, operate it for him too."

Masaaki Nose doesn't know how to run a railroad, but he's in perfect tune with Ito's formula for running a profitable company.

Nose (pronounced "no-say"), a sales veteran who used to be "knee deep in red ink" under the old corporate structure, was assigned in the last decade to the division that is now the Social Infrastructure Systems Company. His job was marketing: selling electrical systems and components. But within the division there were in fact nine separate Toshiba sales subsidiaries, each selling specialized parts and machines of different types, under the general heading of industrial products.

This was from days of yore a classical product strength for Toshiba, which is noted for its strong electrical motors that power pumps, blowers, machine drives, food processing equipment, injector machines, cranes, compressors, industrial air conditioners "and so on."

Under the hodge-podge sales organization that had sprouted at Toshiba as customers and their technologies came and went, this champion product field reported losses from all ten sales organizations totaling four billion yen in 1999 alone.

Now, Toshiba has reorganized its equally fragmented manufacturing units into a single, independent subsidiary, and followed through by aligning all the sales units into a second, equally independent subsidiary.

As a result, Nose and his staff of 600, operating all over Japan, now offer a catalog of 20,000 different product codes: everything Toshiba makes or can make. And any of his sales personnel can sell any or all of them, to any customer who wants to buy.

"This is the kind of product range we wanted, and this accounts for our new success," says Nose. "Under the old system, each sales company could each only sell the products of its own divisions. Now we can cross any category lines and sell all the products. We can manufacture our own products. We can order products from other companies, if Toshiba doesn't make them.

"For example – take these two servo motors, which linked with a controller can make a complete customer solution. All made by Toshiba, all now sold by one company – us – to one customer. Before, we could only sell them one part at a time."

So how do they like you now? "In our first year of business as a new company, we went from a four billion yen loss to a thirty million yen profit. We completely sold out of all our motors!"

But the trepidatious beginning is just as important to this story as the happy ending. What made Toshiba realize reorganization was the solution to the problem?

"We did. In fact it was our own solution, suggested by ten or twenty of us from all the subsidiaries and the main company. We believed that to be combined and independent was the only way to build an efficient and profitable management.

"The younger managers had some misgivings about it. But we at the senior levels were confident. Yes, we knew there was a possibility that if nothing changed and losses kept up we wouldn't be fired, but we might have to change divisions or even be seconded to outside dealers. It was a career risk." For no one more than Nose himself, who as senior sales manager was picked to be company president of the new firm.

"The corporate senior executives we took our plan to were at first worried about it, I think. But they didn't stop us. We got to present our proposal to the boss himself, the head of Social Infrastructure Systems. And of course that man was none other than our corporate president today, Okamura-san. He put the power behind our idea. And in the very first year, all the worries were resolved."

Worries can and will come back; that's the nature of business. But with a management team willing to stake its own careers on its combined skills and determination, one somehow feels just as confident as they that Toshiba motors will be ringing up profits again, for many business cycles to come.

And, Toshiba hopes, so might the independent new school of managers it is trying to foster throughout the corporation.

CHAPTER SIX
THE POWER

Toshiba Corp. has signed a 100-billion-yen deal to supply 34 thermal power generators over three years to California-based . . . Calpine Corp . . . The company [Toshiba] holds a 10% share of the North American market for heavy electrical machinery, putting it in third spot.

Nikkei Weekly
10 September 2001

Toshiba executives, pondering how to plan for their corporation's next leg of growth, needn't look further for one sound resource than its own history. The Power Systems & Services Co., which is the very foundation of Toshiba Corp., is still growing, regularly and handsomely. A sales total of about 4.5 billion dollars was forecast for the fiscal year ending in March 2002.

And as the third largest supplier of its specialty, heavy generators and heavy turbines to drive them, to the US and as the number one supplier of both thermal and nuclear power-plant machinery in Japan, the company and its small fleet of subsidiaries, employing 14,000 altogether, seem to have growth written all over their future.

No extra push will be needed to globalize this arm of Toshiba, which has installed thermal power plants or the main works of them in 31 nations so far, and supplied hydraulic power-plant assemblies in 30. With the world's population forecast to rise to

7 billion by the year 2010, total world power demand is expected to go up by 60%. Export orders alone were expected to more than double within the single year of 2001.

What accounts for all this strength? Toshiba's forebear company was founded on the new technology of electricity: it manufactured Japan's first electric incandescent bulb in 1890, produced its first water-wheel generator in 1894, and turned out its first AC power generator in the same year. Toshiba invented the technique for frosting the interior of light bulbs and built Japan's first 40-ton electric locomotive. It was the electrical business that led Toshiba to form its strong ties with General Electric.

"One of the weaknesses of Toshiba is that our fundamental businesses in industrial and social infrastructure fields, both supposedly stable, have very low levels of profitability," says Toshiba Corp. President Okamura, pointing out that the time for more internationalization in businesses such as Power Systems & Services is at hand. "We believe we can develop such areas fully utilizing IT systems and applying them in traditional areas of electrical power generation," to develop more demand in overseas markets – especially in developing economies such as China's.

Japan derives as much as 36% of its electricity from the atom (50% in Tokyo's case[1]), and a third of that generating capacity was built and installed by Toshiba. Japan's ten power-generating utilities are, together, Toshiba's biggest client group, spending up to four billion dollars per year with the Power Systems & Service Co.

Strategy is reforming the landscape in the more prosaic fields of the industry too. In September 1999, Toshiba and Mitsubishi Electrical Corp. combined in an 800-personnel-strong partnership to jointly use core competencies of both in building large-scale industrial electrical motors. TMA Electric Corp., as this venture is known, has quickly achieved Toshiba's gold-standard target: it is ranked now as the number three company in the world in its field.

And Toshiyuki Oshima, president of Power Systems & Services, is confident that Toshiba's alliance-making strategies, together with new demand in a familiar industry, can open vistas of opportunity even wider. "Will America again become an active market for nuclear power equipment? Yes, I believe so."

American utilities have 103 commercial nuclear power plants now, providing 20% of that country's electricity – and no new units have been built for 20 years, the result of the atomic scare given Americans by the Three-Mile Island accident in 1979.[2]

A press report in the spring of 2001 said the Nuclear Regulatory Agency, the part of the US government which oversees atomic power plants, revealed that some 40% of all such plants in America have made public the fact they will request license renewals rather than shut down the worn-out plants. The NRA said it expected that figure might eventually double.[3]

If granted, those permits would make a huge market in the US for nuclear plants, coming more or less all at once.

Toshiba has formed a three-way engineering alliance with Hitachi (the third-ranked supplier in Japan) and GE, to update the plans and blueprints for the Advanced Boiling Water Reactor, a unit first installed by Toshiba for Tokyo Electric Power in 1996. By 2015 the three partners should be ready to install a 1.7-million-kW kit, producing 30% more power per unit than present models.[4]

A decade and a half is a long time to develop any business, but meanwhile, the company has proposals to install 41 more Boiling Water Reactors in the domestic market, once Japan's nuclear-plant construction programs resume.

And there's all the other business of keeping Japan provided with the electric power it needs. The company's Power Systems Operations in Fuchu concentrates on highly sophisticated monitoring and control systems and equipment for electric power systems, power plant and power utilities.

NOTES

1. "Nuclear energy policy in limbo," Kyodo News Service, carried on *Japan Today* website, 7 September 2001
2. "Japan firms snag nuclear jobs in US," *Nikkei Weekly*, Tokyo, 25 June 2001
3. "Nuclear Power Is Poised for a Comeback," *Washington Post* National Weekly Edition, Washington, 30 April–6 May 2001
4. *Nikkei Weekly*, ibid.

THE TOSHIO DOKO ERA
(1965–1973)

It is hardly possible to explain Japan's economic advance from the
1950s to now without reference to the roles Mr. Doko played . . . The
man was a genius at organizing and administering.

Editorial page, *Asahi Evening News*
August 1988

And also, he was pretty handy as a street sweeper, his neighbors
knew.

Toshio Doko, also born a farmer's son, was one of those rare,
strong men who has seemed to come along just at the time
Toshiba needed rescuing by a leader of very special abilities.

The man was in the right place: joining what became the
world's largest shipbuilder, Ishikawajima–Harima, fresh out of
engineering school in 1920, he had become not only that corporation's president, but a member of the board of Toshiba
by 1965.

And the corporation was in the wrong place: after the burst
of spending for the 1964 Tokyo Olympics, the economy had
momentarily burned itself out, leaving Toshiba way overex-
tended, in debt, and ineptly managed by executives of the "old
school" – the kind who didn't bother to report to their offices
until 9.30 or 10 each day.

As he was about to leave the chairmanship of Toshiba and
move on to the presidency of Keidanren, Taizo Ishizaka took a
shuddering look at the challenges Toshiba was facing, knew it

was unprepared for them, and asked Doko to step in as president, to save the company.

"And Doko came in," is how one of the specialists who are now compiling an official history of Toshiba puts it. "He wanted to show an example of what it means to work hard, to all the other Toshiba executives."

He must have made a great exemplar, because in a sense Toshio Doko's day never ended. He rose at 4 each morning, shaved using the same brush he had used for fifty years, then sat at the family's small Buddhist altar to read sutras. After that he practiced Japanese fencing exercises in his garden, then weeded the plot of vegetables in which he and his wife grew all their radishes. Then it was the morning papers – until the 6 a.m. television news – and a light breakfast, a trip to the office, and finally the business day began at 7 a.m.

He kept his office door open for the first 90 minutes of each day, so that any employee with a subject to discuss might simply walk through it. He visited his 31 plants unannounced, traveling alone, to step out on the assembly floor and talk to engineers and workers about the job and about their lives.

Not only did he straighten out (or clean out) the regiments of top managers whose own leadership styles were so casual, but he righted the company organizationally and – very notably – became one of the few presidents of his day to take the whole company off rigid seniority-based management, and move it towards a merit system which gave more importance to job performance. He took away all but formal personnel authority from administrative departments, and gave on-the-job powers to the factory floor units and the immediate supervisors in Toshiba's offices.

As a business magazine of the day put it, "In a radical break with the Japanese tradition of promotion by seniority, he cut out the bureaucratic deadwood, did away with sectionalism, and created a 'grand staff' of directors answerable only to himself. He also decreed that Toshiba must not rely on foreign technology but develop its own know-how."[1]

It was Doko who, relying on knowledge he had gained in researching nuclear-power technology in his Ishikawajima-Harima days, first steered Toshiba, as its president, into the crucial field of atomic power plant engineering.

When asked who in the Toshiba of his younger days influenced him the most, President Okamura quickly presents two names: those of founder Hisashige Tanaka, and Toshio Doko. The latter "showed extremely strong leadership in wiping away the bureaucratic mentality that existed back then in Toshiba, prevailing throughout the company. And after being president of Toshiba, he became Keidanren chairman, and was very instrumental in pushing forward national administrative reform [by serving on special committees] of the government."

"He had a clear vision of how this company had to perform," smiles Chairman Nishimuro, "and how all those sleepy employees had to be woken up."

President (and later chairman) Doko even had his own little book of sayings, which was briefly a bestseller among Japanese businessmen: "Envision the future clearly," read one. "This will encourage hope in others."

"A creative company," he explained, "invariably possesses a vision for its own future. And its employees, conscious of the objectives, can then decide their own individual reasons for being part of this effort, and let their own creativity unfold."

They were good words for Toshiba, then and now.

They had the kind of sturdy principles he himself lived by, as his neighbors could see. In Japanese neighborhoods it was tradition for members of all families to turn out of a morning now and then, and sweep the public walkways and roadsides in front of their homes. Still it was a surprise to see, on frequent occasions, that one of the street sweepers was also one of Japan's most powerful captains of industry and economic leadership, Toshio Doko.

You couldn't say he died poor, though in his years as Toshiba's chairman, when his salary was somewhere around 60 million yen per year, he donated almost all of it to a charitable school for women founded thirty years before by his deeply devout Buddhist mother.

But probably you could say he was content when he did pass on. At the age of 90, he published these words to the world: "I would like to express my gratitude. I have lived a life of 90 years reckoned by a motto, 'Don't look back. Today is a new day.' "[2]

He died at 92. The prime minister, the former prime minister, the chairman of Keidanren, and 10,000 others came to his funeral.

It was Toshio Doko who put Toshiba on the organizational track to become the high-tech company that it had to become, to move ahead on the next wave of Japan's prosperity in the late 1960s, and to stay in the top ranks of creativity where competitors both new and old were already trying to elbow it aside.

NOTES

1. *Business Japan*, Tokyo, October 1971
2. Kaichiro Shimura, *Toshio Doko – Legacy Toward the 21st Century*, Bunshun Bunko, Tokyo, January 1988

CHAPTER SEVEN
IN THE BEGINNING WAS THE WORD

Maybe it started with the badminton – you know, the little white shuttlecock, the point of light dancing back and forth, back and forth, like the "follow-the-bouncing-ball" on a movie screen, when everybody's supposed to sing along but can't remember the words until they appear on the screen, matched up to the music by that little white point.

Or maybe not. Maybe it was just the fact that, despite he and his middle-school buddies loving the sport so much, they could never find a printed set of badminton rules, and in the end he had to translate a whole booklet of them from English into Japanese.

But anyway, Kenichi Mori was thinking about words, and how to move them from symbols to action, long before he was thinking about girls.

Mori went some way beyond middle school – to a BS in physics, then a Ph.D. from the nation's most prestigious post-graduate institution, the University of Tokyo – before joining Toshiba in 1962 as a rookie in the Corporate Research & Development Center.

He's been around a little since then, having by today worked his way up to President of Toshiba TEC Corp., the largest of the Toshiba subsidiaries, with 5,600 employees and 340 billion yen in annual revenues.

But oh, what a journey it's been! Along the way, among other things, he invented Chinese character-recognition by machine, and incidentally, the Japanese-language word processor. And he's still fooling with the idea of trying to perfect the machine translator.

When, of course, he's not overseeing the manufacture and sale of Toshiba's copy machines. Or figuring out new ways to bring the mastery of data analysis to small shops and offices at an affordable price. (Toshiba TEC is the largest maker and seller of Point-of-Sale systems in Japan, with almost a third of the national market – and it is the market leader in France as well. As such, the company is on the cutting edge of integrating POS cash-register, accounting, stock-tracking and similar automated functions into complete information technology systems for small- and medium-sized businesses all over Japan.)

But wait – we'd better begin at the beginning.

That was back in the R&D Center in 1962, when as the new man on the block he was assigned to a team researching ways to improve magnetic memory engineering. Brash as any young man with his credentials, he sketched out a number of approaches to the problem. Then, doing a literature review, he discovered that every one of them had already been thought of, and was being investigated somewhere else. Not much of a start.

"So I wanted to find a very new research topic." Thanks to a short paper that a friend of his was developing, describing some work at Bell Laboratories, the concept of "character recognition" came up. "Their project was to develop a machine that could read a handwritten character. He asked me just what they meant by machine-reading of letters, so I cast around – but I couldn't find any papers or articles that described the details of pattern recognition. So I thought, this might make a very good research topic!"

Good or not, it would be a tricky one for Toshiba's R&D arm. The English language trades on only 26 letters (52, if you count capitals), a handful of punctuation marks, and ten numeric symbols. Japanese uses four separate orthographies, including two phonetic syllaberies, called *hiragana* and *katakana*, of 51 characters each, the English alphabet, and the subset of Chinese ideographs called by the Japanese *kanji*. Literacy generally requires knowledge of a minimum of 1,843 *kanji*, but formal-level functionality in the language is a matter of knowing about 5,500.

Each *kanji* is drawn with anywhere from one to 26 separate strokes of the pen, and each renders a different meaning depending on how it is used with the characters around it.

Well, if every Japanese can master literacy by high school, and the challenge was really just to recognize one character at a time – how difficult could it be to make a machine do it? Kenichi Mori and colleagues decided to find out.

But Mori was already adding twists to the plot of an unwritten story. As it was written, he wanted Toshiba's machine to recognize the patterns precisely that way: as handwritten. "Machines should serve people," thought Mori, "not the other way around." Since there are thousands of different subtleties in the way millions of different people hand-write all those strokes, he thought the machine couldn't really serve human society unless it could recognize the handwriting of *any* human.

"We started with the obvious way. We figured how a machine would do it, and that is how we set it up. Machines – crude computers of that day – were lineal in the way they processed information: 1 + 1 = 2. You wanted to input data, you punched holes in a bunch of paper cards and slid them along the line while the machine recognized the pattern on each."

Simple enough: a square screen was created, with the character shown on it in a pattern of white dots. The machine traveled slavishly, one by one, along lines that crossed the screen horizontally, stacked atop each other top to bottom, as if reading with its finger. It noted either a "1" or a "0" depending on whether or not there was a mark in any short interval along any of the lines. By the last line, bottom right, it had electronically assembled an image of the whole character that the dots presented, which it then compared to images stored in its memory until it found a match.

So that it did not have to compare what it had recognized to every one of the thousands of characters in its memory, the machine was given a ten-step logic chain, to first eliminate what the character *couldn't* be. The correct character, once matched, was loaded into any output device, ready to be delivered ex machina in the same sequence in which it had been read.

But – so what? Oh yes, the device could read simple postal codes – and did so in the line of duty, when Toshiba delivered an automatic mail-sorting device to the Central Post Office in 1967.

But humans are notoriously slovenly, quirky, different. As noted, they each write the same character, even a simple one, in a different way. If they put a stroke in a character a little too high or too low to be read on the correct line by the machine – the machine lost the whole character because it just didn't "know" where to turn for the misplaced part that would complete the picture. For example, if I wrote Shizuoka on one envelope, each letter would look very different to the machine from the

SHIZUOKA I write on the next envelope.

"So we knew we had to find another idea, a method in which the machine could handle a two-dimensional object two-dimensionally" – by moving up or down, side to side, to locate *all* the strokes marked there.

Eventually, they did it by modifying the grid: they made it 15 lines high by 15 lines across, making every intersection a grid mark – and thus every image, a collection of 225 geometrically spaced data points. They gave the machine a small TV-camera tube to read these points and pass them two-dimensionally to the memory, which "graded" how closely the sloppy, crooked, or streaked character, writ large or small, resembled the real character stored there. Some complicated sampling math was needed.

But now the postal scanners Toshiba built could read the whole hand-written address, whether it was from Maya-san to Kenji-san, inviting the latter to a birthday party at the playground, or from Professor Kuniyama to Doctor Miyazaki, inviting the latter to a research seminar at Hitotsubashi University.

So what? The machine, Mori's team of colleagues, now grown to 30 researchers, knew, still *understood* nothing of what it read.

"Our final goal, by now, had become something different. We wanted to exchange information through the machine . . . We wanted the machine to recognize the meaning of our sentences. And we wanted, finally, for it to translate that meaning correctly into another language, and then receive a reply and translate it back into correct Japanese."

What they really wanted was the grail of linguistics, a machine translator.

Now Toshiba, having achieved pattern recognition and having realized the actual product that corporate research ultimately aims for – in this case, a postal address sorter – was not really sure it wanted to test its own abilities, not to say resources, on a new search for this grail (these quests often ending, as they do, in less than complete success).

So Mori and his colleagues, now shrunk to four friends including Tsutomu Kawada, resorted to the last sanction in the R&D collocation of job priorities, the notorious "under-the-table" seminar. As long as researchers carry their weight in Toshiba's designated projects, they are allowed a small increment of company time and resources, and all they want of their own personal time and resources, to pursue The Impossible Dream.

Mori laughs now. "When we have a research conundrum the solving of which seems to have no obvious corporate benefit in sight, or that seems to be insoluble or beyond our capability, we call it a 'monkey problem.' That means, you know, it is like an onion to a monkey: he believes there's something good to reach on the inside, but the more he peels away the layers, the more layers he finds – until at last he comes to nothing at all. When we have a monkey problem, we take it under the table."

It is a management device that, though Toshiba's eloquent engineer-managers and research directors might not put it this way, keeps young researchers from getting bored.

So under the table, they reasoned thus: "The first step in building a machine translator was to develop a good Japanese typewriter – an input device." There were, in the business world, only bulky, type-setter-like machines in which a skilled operator picked out a cast die of each exact character, swung a metal arm over it, and punched down on a lever to stamp the character on paper. Obviously that technology led nowhere.

"So we knew we had to develop a keyboard that could somehow input the characters of Japanese and all their subtle meanings in accord with their usage in the syntax of the actual text. Plus we had to give it a big memory – and we had to make it portable!"

Tall orders. Answered not soon, but soon enough. The Japanese language when read yields of course the syllables we actually hear. And almost every character in which it is written represents a complete syllable. The most common Japanese word for "connection" is *kankei*, which is written with two Chinese characters, the first pronounced "kan" and the second "kei." So, using the common phonetic alphabet of 51 phonetic characters which every Japanese is taught in the first grade, it's very simple to arrange 51 keys, each with a syllable on it. Tap the four correct keys, and the phonetic characters for "ka," "n," "ke," and "i" appear on the screen, the paper, or whatever output device one chooses.

(Computers had of course been introduced, but were nowhere near in popular use in Japan at that time, 1971.)

But – it is very hard for even a Japanese to read a whole sentence that is printed phonetically. Why? Because the same sounds, "kan" and "kei," joined together have alternate meanings to "connection": taken just by sound, they could represent the words for a type of warship, a trick, a laconic style of speaking, the return of the Crown Prince, a stem of grass, or a plumbing diagram. The only way to be sure which meaning is intended by the sounds is to visually read the Chinese characters. The characters used to write "kankei" are different for each of the meanings listed in the sentence before last.

The under-the-table gang finally solved the problem by applying computer technology. Due to expanding chip speeds and memories, they could build a machine with software that, when a typist entered the phonetic symbols for "kankei," would automatically and immediately cast up the full vocabulary list of all words pronounced that way, showing the correct Chinese characters for each of them, in descending order of common use in everyday speech.

For example the characters for "connection" would be shown on top of the list on the screen, and below them the characters for "trick," and then below those the characters for "plumbing diagram," and so on.

The operator had but to point the cursor at the word he or she intended, and click. The correct Chinese characters were automatically added to the sentence being written at the top of the screen.

★

As Mori's development project lasted until 1978, advances in computing power provided solutions to such other problems as a need for large and fast memory for storage, and small size for the machine (though the first ones that came to market were as big as desks). Sophisticated editing functions, stylistic typography, fast printing, and all the tricks of the computer world were soon added.

The Toshiba product stepped into the market as Japan's first word processor, in 1979, just in time for the dawn of the personal computer age and, somewhat later, the spread of the Internet. And by 1980 the monkey's problem had come so far out from under the table that Doctor Mori was given the Minister of State for Science and Technology Award by the government "for research and development of the Japanese word processor."

Somebody else would likely have invented that word processor if Mori hadn't, it's true. Because it was needed. Without it the Japanese would have continued faxing each other pages of paper, and so would have missed the entire Internet revolution. Today of course, personal computers that are Japanese-character capable are ubiquitous, and Mori's team's invention is now as insubstantial and transparent as a piece of software downloadable onto a disk, or loaded into cell phones that connect to the Internet, via a chip in the handset programmed both for Chinese ideographs and the two Japanese phonetic syllaberies, plus the Roman alphabet.

But it's still a patent that belongs to Toshiba, and that has linked its destiny that much more firmly with the evolution of IT in Japan.

About the machine translation technology, the grail, a soft-spoken Mori waxes philosophical. "Eventually I was moved up to business administration. But my team, headed by Doctor Kawada, kept at it, and they produced a very good software for

Japanese-to-English-to-Japanese. Won a prize, I believe. It's true we still haven't gotten completely there. And it's true the word processor is just a by-product of our search for a machine translator. But it may be a very valuable by-product to Japanese society. Many people have said I chose at the time a target that was a true monkey problem, one with no perfect solution possible.

"But what's the point of technology? It's to be useful to human society – not to prove some point of mathematical perfection." Beyond all question, his word processor hit the "useful" criterion right on the nose.

Mori is just happy that Toshiba is now able to work with Chinese researchers to see if the same technology can be useful in building a simple Chinese word processor, too. "We will make no money off this Chinese collaboration," Mori insists. "Two thousand years ago we Japanese borrowed the Chinese ideographic alphabet to be able to write our language. It's time we paid them back in some small way."

His own real reward, he's still getting under the table. It's hard to take time away from managing Toshiba's biggest subsidiary – but whenever he can, he meets the young, bright-eyed crew of Corporate R&D Center staff who are still interested in machine translation (and there are several), and tries to pose challenges for them, by pointing to new paths toward the frontiers of the science, and inviting them to track these.

"Our team is still working on problems of human grammar. But, I ask them, what is the 'grammar' of the human genome? Recently scientists have found the number of basic genes in humans is only 30,000 to 40,000. Think of it – so few components to build this structure, a human? Some rule, some structure, for the arrangement of these may exist that comes close to the structure of human-language grammar. It may be built into us genetically, this ability to construct languages."

Does he hope to decrypt a genetic code for language some

day? "I just hope that I can continue to stimulate their creativity, those young researchers."

When asked about lessons and guidance learned from his Toshiba mentors over the years, Corporate President Okamura is quick to bring up the name of Kenichi Mori, "the father of the first Japanese word processor. He is an excellent computer science engineer, of course. But in order to develop that system, he needed really to be able to understand at a very deep level Japanese culture. And so he has these two different aspects. I have a deep, deep respect for him. He is a friend of mine. He and I are the same age. We meet even now three or four times a year, and we discuss many things about how to manage our own organizations."

Stimulating leadership creativity mightily, one might imagine.

CHAPTER EIGHT
A NEED TO KNOW:
iVALUE CREATION CO.

Tsutomu Kawada was inspired in the mid 1970s by his boss, Kenichi Mori, to create the input system for the country's first Japanese-language word processor. It was 20 years later and 8,000 miles away when the boss of another company inspired him to take his next major step in the technology of communications.

Kouji Ohboshi, president of a new Japanese company called NTT DoCoMo, was breezing through the pages of the *Nihon Keizai Shimbun*, Japan's most famous business journal, one day while on a business trip to New York City, when his eye fell on a small item about Toshiba. So far never having made any kind of mobile cellular product, it was apparent that now one of Japan's biggest electronic manufacturers was trying to play catch-up: Toshiba had produced a small hand-held telephone for one of NTT DoCoMo's rivals, KDDI.

Ohboshi, folding the newspaper page carefully and pocketing it, decided then and there it was time to step in and investigate this new partnership, before it could become a serious rival to his own company.

Once back in Japan, he did just that by paying a visit to Kawada, who had spearheaded development of the tiny new phone, to make him an offer he couldn't refuse: take a concept that Ohboshi had – something like a pocket-size, hand-held computer that was also a telephone and an Internet terminal – and make it real.

Kawada was intrigued. "I couldn't find, as I worked, any good information on mixing all these technologies, in miniature form. So I decided at the same time as I was designing to develop a good library of technical information *and* some good applications for it."

What he ended up producing was a clunker. "It was too big and boxy to be used as a telephone," he laughs now. "Especially for ladies. And also the cost of using it was horrendous – in those days all mobile phone devices had to use a direct switch connection-based technology, which meant a direct, full-time cellular channel. To search the Internet, let alone to just browse, from a mobile phone meant connection times that cost a fortune."

That was in 1998, still young days for mobile communication in Japan. But two things were about to happen in rapid succession. The first was that NTT DoCoMo was to quickly apply a technology of packet switching to mobile phones. This meant the information that cell phone and cell switch exchanged with each other, and with the Internet, was bunched into data groups and sent down the channel (or down several channels) very fast, discretely and mixed in line with other packets for all sorts of other connections – like machine-gun bullets fired at digital speed, but with each bullet aimed at a different target.

With this technology, NTT DoCoMo also made available an information channel direct from any cell-phone subscriber to the Internet – a product called i-mode. Available to all cell phones in the NTT DoCoMo service stable, i-mode enabled electronic vendors to plan business offerings of goods and services via the Internet, straight to the hands of cell-phone users, wherever they happened to be at the moment they dialed up.

And the second thing that happened was that Kawada caught Internet fever.

While the engineers of Toshiba Mobile Communications

Company took up the battle to make more and better mobile phones and connection technologies, Toshiba launched its in-house iValue Creation Company, in April 2000, to explore ways to enter the businesses of information services that would be offered on those mobile devices. Kawada, with his background in linguistics and electrical engineering, was thinking deeply about what, beyond conversation, a mobile telephone might deliver to its user when it is hooked directly to the Internet. The answer, he realized, depended only on how wide his own imagination was.

He recognized cellular phones were now an entirely new medium, a new business space wide open to new products. He fit the bill as the perfect president of the new in-house company, with a mandate to create entirely new businesses that would fit into the infrastructure of Internet and mobile Internet. The most inviting fields of this new world were application service provision, e-commerce and businesses-to-consumer trade, especially those transactions with an air of immediacy that mobile communications fits: travel requirements, finance, even music broadcast by Internet.

Kawada had long been burning to fill the shelves in this new market. Before iValue was even a company, he thought about all sorts of new and different services, never seen before, that he could make and sell on the Internet. Something that would launch Toshiba's name as a big-time player on that same Internet. "We talked over amongst ourselves what typical cell-phone users might want. And we realized one thing we all had in common was that we were job commuters, who took trains and subways a lot each day. We often found ourselves lost on the way to a new customer's office, or looking for a good restaurant in a strange neighborhood."

The solution was a brilliant mix of text and graphics that could all be called up on the tiny cell-phone screen: *Eki-mae Tanken*

Club, it was called, or station-area explorer. You could call up for example a map of the area, large-scale or small, around almost any station in Tokyo, input your needs – to find a building, a big store, a French restaurant, even a hotel – and get not only directions to it from the station, but information such as prices and services offered. You could even *book* a hotel through this new Club.

The idea caught on like wildfire. The service is deliverable on the mobile phones of all three competing cell-phone service companies in Japan, but by far the largest, NTT DoCoMo, came to Toshiba with a special invitation, extended directly to Toshiba from NTT DoCoMo's project chief, to add the *Eki-mae Tanken* Club to the i-mode list of registered suppliers.

"*Eki-mae Tanken* is famous now," says Kawada. And so, it's made its new home, iValue Creation Co., famous along with it. "We've got 360,000 subscribers, at 100 yen each per month." It sinks in after only a second: 100 yen each per month? That means the whole business is worth only 432 million yen per year. Three and a half million dollars a year income, on the most famous product turned out by one of the ten key companies in a 50-billion-dollars-per-year corporation? Plus, there's an overhead for constantly refreshing the prices, and other information on the site, and for . . .

"Yes, it runs in the red," smiles Kawada, undaunted. "But it's far from our only product." Actually he started a business-to-business Web service as early as 1996, tag-named NewsWatch, in which 80 English-language news or specialty publications are covered in abstract each day, and full texts are delivered to paying subscribers. "This quarter, it just went into the black. It's my first profitable-product success with iValue." This is a goal that was achieved, it deserves to be noted, less than a year after the new company had been called into being.

★

The NewsWatch concept has, however, also been a bridge to customized services of a similar nature tailored for a dozen big corporate customers, such as pharmaceuticals makers, who must stay abreast of global developments in their industries on a day-by-day basis. The electronic clip-and-translate service fed into these corporate customers' portable computers is proprietary, and thus much more high-margin.

And still more interesting is the on-line mobile trading system iValue has developed for Matsui Securities Co. Ltd., where clients dial in daily for quotes and to make stock-market buys and sells.

iValue of course wouldn't be the first on-line service provider to suffer financial losses in the tangled game of mobile communications, nor would Kawada be the first venture interpreneur (for that is exactly what he is) to kiss an avalanche of capital goodbye trying to find a suitable business model. But he does have Toshiba's resources, and its patience, to back him up. So he can go on thinking up new i-for-Internet Values, and look for the customers out there, corporate or consumer, who will pay by the hundreds of yen or by the billion to use them. It takes time. They've giving him time.

Consider the models it relies upon: Toshiba long ago became half-owner of Toshiba-EMI Ltd., which controls one-quarter of the music business in Japan – even though Toshiba long ago stopped making any consumer audio equipment. And Toshiba watched Kawada, Mori, and their few posse members struggle with and finally deliver a hallmark product of its epoch, the Japanese word processor.

Toshiba sank a lot of capital getting to top rank in the market in each case. Now, with a new medium and new market to deliver the product in, it intends to go on reeling in the payback from both: words and music for mobile distribution. "We are even thinking of a way to download recordable music via mobile phone, so users can listen and make their own records of any music they want while they shop, while they eat, while they commute."

Right now iValue is focusing, under Kawada's eye, on the more proven area of just this kind of content sales, business-to-business and business-to-consumer, over mobile phones. A full-dimension mobile commerce is the model. "It's our next project, to fit the user's activities perfectly. We can find his or her location exactly with GPS positioning satellite, refer to his or her profile on record, and recommend the nearest stores or entertainment centers, and tell which ones have the best attractions and prices on the products the user is interested in. Location-sensitive, time-sensitive, and personalization-sensitive is all coming, drawing everything we can do all together."

Big-time money-making ideas? Using satellites to tell someone where to go to get ten per cent off a designer scarf? Who knows – someone will sign up, someone else will copy them, soon enough if they prove out. But by then, Kawada plans to be already moving on to the next new product, in his own market of ideas.

CHAPTER NINE
MOBILE NETWORKS

Canberra (AP) The electronic tweeting of mobile phones is so wide-spread that some Australian birds are mimicking the sound as part of their mating and territorial songs, bird experts say.

Japan Times
14 June 2001

If the famous mimic birds of Australia are confused by the world's current plethora of mobile telephones, you could perhaps forgive electronics and telecom firms' strategic planners for being unable to see the global picture clearly themselves.

No shoals were more treacherous, no seas were foggier than those navigated in the early 2000s by mobile-telephone competitors – both equipment makers and carriers – casting their fates out across the broad technological seas that separate country from country, region from region, in the race to build (or join) the world's first global pocket-phone network.

Some have already thrown it over: Dutch giant Philips announced in mid 2001 it was simply exiting the mobile phone manufacturing business.[1] Some have sought partnerships for sheer protection: Telefon AB LM Ericsson joined its unprofitable phone cell business with Sony's two months previously;[2] and some have chosen technological cooperation: NEC and Matsushita Electric Industrial revealed in August 2001 a tie-up to develop and test next-generation products. In order, the two are already Japan's No. 1 and No. 2 handset makers, but still seem to feel a need for synergy as expense risk grows.

For this last fact alone, it seems strange to hear Tetsuya Mizoguchi, company president of Toshiba's Mobile Communications Co., say that "Digital, Mobile, and Network are key words for the new Toshiba. It's all based on the IT revolution." Strange because Toshiba only commanded 2.3% of the world market in 2000 (less than half of even Samsung's share), and openly admits it missed its chance for the present generation – the so-called 2G phone technology – right in its home market. "The game is over; we're not really part of that," sighs Shigekazu Hori, Mobile Comm's Chief Technology Executive.

So why, suddenly, are mobile phones The Future at tenth-ranked Toshiba?

For a number of tactical reasons:

First, Toshiba has not been able to become a bigger player in its own home market. There are three mobile-phone operators in Japan, and by far the largest is NTT DoCoMo, which has almost 60% of Japan's 62 million cell-phone subscribers. The carriers determine who will supply the actual phones to their customers, and they are so much in charge that they will not even permit a manufacturer to put its own brand logo on the phone it supplies. So far NTT DoCoMo has not accepted Toshiba on its supply list; however in 3G technology (FOMA), Toshiba will be a handset supplier to NTT DoCoMo.

Second, notwithstanding, Toshiba has skyrocketed its production of handsets, doubling the total from four to eight million just in the three years 1998–2000. Part of that has been big chunks of supply to NTT DoCoMo's two Japanese competitors – and half, or four million units, have been sales just in the year 2000 to the United States. Toshiba *does* know how to make a good phone, *and* how to sell it.

Third, the global market, though seemingly saturated already, really isn't. Japan's nationwide potential market was already 50% penetrated in 2001, and still absorbing growth of about 10% per year.[3] The US market penetration is about the same.[4] With some predicting the Asia–Pacific market for cell phones will more than double from 250 million to 550 million by 2004,[5] there's still a great swath of market growth open to competition.

Fourth and most important, a new technology is about to be born, one whose principal feature will be global interoperability (get on a plane and fly anywhere; you can call anywhere else on earth from wherever you are), but which will also be packed with extras like Internet access, large-scale memory capacity, and even live video transmission. The replacement demand from present users alone, once this new technology is on the market, will run into the tens of millions of units.

And that brings Toshiba to one big strategic reason for getting into the field. The new technology, buzz-named 3G for now, will completely enable the Digital, Mobile, and Networks that Mizoguchi mentioned. These 3G phones will offer video connections to one another: you have a built-in camera on your phone, that takes any picture you want in full-color motion and sends it to the display panel on your friend's phone, on-line, to show it. This kind of technology made its world debut on the frontlines of Afghanistan, where early-arrival TV correspondents used it to send their own "live spots" back to the studio.

It will have still-picture and of course e-mail. It will handle banking, and ticketing – whether for a baseball game or a flight to Honolulu. It will deliver 24-hour news; it will deliver video programming or musical programming on demand.

It will have always-on Internet access. If you don't know the Web-page address of the site you want to see, it will have a bar-code reader that matches a small directory in your purse or pocket: just pass the reader over the bar-code address on the directory's page, and the phone immediately opens the Web page. Those things are here now, in demonstration models, in Toshiba.

But it can also be a go-anywhere commuter railroad ticket: just punch in your destination, and swipe the phone across the electronic ticket gate when you embark at any station. It will be a wallet: dial up the soft-drink machine in front of you, and it will dispense a cold drink – billing your bank account simultaneously. It will be a key: just point it and wave it at your front-door lock.

These are things that will be done – in Japan, they'll be done with software created at least in part by Tsutomu Kawada and his iValue Co. – as soon as the Digital, Mobile, and Network is in place.

And when will that be? Chicken and egg: the phones will come in first, followed by the services that will be offered through the broadband, high-speed technology by the carriers and then by the on-line service providers.

Sound drearily complicated? To the engineers, it is. Sound like a risky business? To the executives, even more so. Many companies, particularly in Europe, have strained themselves dangerously paying for rights to bandwidth, and paying to prepare for service that hasn't even arrived yet. NTT DoCoMo, determined to be the first operator in the world to offer 3G, planned to open it in the spring of 2001 but delayed it until the autumn due to the recall of more than a million new handsets that proved to have bugs, a series of embarrassing flops that cost millions of dollars.

And still it runs rocky. "The number of software-related checkpoints [that must be tested] has now reached as many as 200,000," says a Tokyo business weekly of the debugging challenge, "as carriers have to scramble to incorporate new functions ranging from Internet access to the capability to download music and games from the Net, making cell phones more like personal computers."[6]

These are the kind of challenges – to other makers – that don't frighten Mizoguchi. Because Toshiba already has the technology, and the expertise in it, to avoid the mistakes that others are making. "These are technologies for IT revolution," says Mizoguchi, and he and his company have been in that revolution for a long time already, he points out.

In a sense, more than half of Toshiba's corporate structure is now aligned, like rabbet joints in fine cabinetry, to fit precisely together with the digital media network. "Semiconductor, Display Devices and Components, e-Solution, iValue and the Digital Media Network Companies, and my own Mobile Communications Company to bring them all together: the mobile arena will make many new systems.

"There is so much feedback and interplay between products as they develop. So for that reason we're already making a new digital mobile network development center, at our Ome plant, which will completely realign our engineering specialties to attack the problems from all sides.

"TV engineers, mobile engineers, wireless engineers, software engineers, optical-media engineers, hard-disk-drive engineers and PC engineers and video engineers – they will all come to work together, three thousand of them, in a single building."

Just to make mobile phones? In the teeth of so much hard competition, isn't Toshiba betting an awful lot on just one product sector?

"But it's not just the mobile phone," says Chief Technology Executive Hori. "The phone is just a first step – the next step is the Personal Digital Assistant [PDA] pocket computer, and the portable computer itself. We're going to work very hard for three years – then come back and see what the real product is!"

"Toshiba's portable computers," adds Mizoguchi, "introduced

in 1985, have been both technology and business drivers for our company ever since. Now the world is changing, especially quickly in the era of mobile communications. It's time for us to continue in a new direction."

That's it. It finally stands clear: Toshiba doesn't think these are "telephones" at all. They are becoming *computers* which are not much larger than cell phones.

Because of wireless, or rather the digital wireless network, all the functions of the new electronic universe can be placed in your hand, in the shape of a simple tool like a pocket telephone. It's supposed to be a little like having not a phone, but an office – a whole business, a whole industry – in your pocket.

As Toshiba looks back over the corporate past that is pointing to its future, it has seen clearly the trend it must not follow, but lead. In 1960, 12% of its business was information and communications systems and electronic devices – the forerunners of the digital age. By 1980, those products were a quarter of Toshiba's business – by 1990, they were more than half.

In the year 2000, IT products constituted 82% of Toshiba's business by net sales. It isn't hard to spot *that* kind of trend. Toshiba has no choice but to plunge into the mobile-communications sea, no matter how murky the waters.

Oh, it has its proven tactics to fall back upon, such as possible main-scale future alliances. And there's always component sales: Toshiba can sell display screens, signal-compression miniature video cameras, 20-gigabyte 1.8 inch HDDs no bigger than a pack of gum, flash memories, and on and on, to whatever other players would rather pay for the quality than develop it themselves.

Toshiba today sells to Sony hard-disk drives, optical-disk DVDs, thin-film transistor displays and semiconductors for Sony's VAIO portable computer. It buys from Sony lithium-ion batteries for its own DynaBook portable computer.

And both companies, competing ferociously head-to-head in the portable PC markets, are happy with their deals – for today. It's a complicated world out there.

But Mizoguchi thinks he knows what it will all come down to. In midsummer, he released Toshiba's first Pocket PC. Most importantly, it has Windows and Microsoft's suite softwares designed for Pocket PC. It has two card-insert slots for flash memories, and supports modem cards, Bluetooth cards, and bar-code readers. It will also support Global Positioning Satellite and Local Area Network cards too, as soon as they're on the market. It delivers 65,536 colors on its 3.5-inch, 77,000-pixel display, weighs six and a third ounces, and was set to debut in the fall in America for $600.

To Mizoguchi, it's beautiful: not so much the future as the next step toward it.

But it does, you'll be forced to admit if you hold it, look an awful lot like a window into tomorrow.

NOTES

1. "Philips Disconnects From the Mobile Phone Business," *International Herald Tribune*, Paris, 27 June 2001
2. "Debut of 3G cell phones sparks tie-ups," *Nikkei Weekly*, Tokyo, 23 April 2001
3. "Mobile Multimedia Evolution in Japan," *Japan Economic Currents*, Tokyo, July 2001
4. "Choosing a Cellphone When Safety Counts as Much as Service," *Wall Street Journal*, New York, 27 September 2001
5. "Asia Sustains Its Appetite for Mobile Phones," *International Herald Tribune*, Paris, 26 June 2001
6. "Sony fumbles on cell-phone quality," *Nikkei Weekly*, Tokyo, 16 July 2001

THE SHOICHI SABA ERA [1980–1987]

... through the 1970s the company was considered an also-ran, trailing other Japanese business groups, known as *keiretsu* partly because of its bureaucratic management style.

Electrical engineer Shoichi Saba became president in 1980. Saba invested heavily in Toshiba's information and communications segments. The company became the first in the world to produce the powerful one-megabit DRAM chip [1985]. That year it unveiled its first portable PC. In the meantime Saba [named chairman 1986] pushed Toshiba into joint ventures to exchange technology with companies such as Siemens and Motorola.

But in 1987 Toshiba incurred the wrath of the US government. A subsidiary sold submarine sound-deadening equipment to the USSR, resulting in threats of US sanctions and a precipitous decline in stock price and in US sales ...

Hoover's Company Profiles[1]

July 2001

"So in only 30 minutes I briefed Mister Saba. He was just sitting there, saying nothing. Just leaning back, listening. He's very fast in his mind so normally, he never listens 30 minutes in a row to somebody on any subject – maybe five minutes is the most. But that day, he was just listening."

Shoichi Saba is still looked on as something of a cross between a hero and Superman in the executive halls of Toshiba Corp.

"Saba-san came from the heavy equipment division [at the behest of former president Toshio Doko]. He had very little knowledge about semiconductors, but he understood my requirement. I asked him to invest a lot of money and he agreed. What he had was vision."

The speaker, retired senior vice-president Tsuyoshi Kawanishi, was the man who took those gambles, placed them on the table, and saw Toshiba emerge as the number one producer of DRAMs, with 45% of the global market, by the close of the Saba decade. "Of all the Toshiba presidents I knew, I think Saba-san was the best."

Another Toshiba executive – the current corporate president, Tadashi Okamura – agrees. "Mister Saba made a real change for Toshiba. It was he who had a real vision for the future in the IT business. He was very instrumental in changing the company's culture because while he had a very warm personality, at the same time he was very sharp and very global-minded."

The subject of all this praise was born in 1919 to a Presbyterian minister in a near-Tokyo suburb called Ohmori. He became a Christian also in his teenage period. As a child he found an interest in science, developing curiosities toward such fields as radio, chemistry, or railroads, and, as he got older, electrical engineering. Playing with household appliances was his favorite hobby. The family radio, with its vacuum tube and trumpet-shaped speaker, was a source of fascination. He was so excited to have access to electric machines in his home that he even experienced a minor electric shock for the first time while playing.[2]

He entered Tokyo Imperial University, as it was then called (now the University of Tokyo), in 1939. He chose a major in Electrical Engineering without hesitation. At that time, war in Europe was expanding and a tense atmosphere had mounted in Japan as well. Upon graduation, he joined Tokyo Shibaura

Electric Company (now Toshiba), and was assigned to the research laboratory. However, one month later he was called up in the draft and began his army experience in the lowest rank in an artillery unit. One year later, he was given new responsibility with the Army's Engineering Office, and taught electrical engineering and wireless communication engineering to cadets at the Army Air Force Academy until the end of the war.

Saba looks back on his experience of having studied wireless engineering as turning out to be very valuable when he returned to Toshiba. In the postwar economic chaos, Toshiba experienced labor disputes for a long period of time, but nonetheless gradually climbed the road to recovery. In the meantime, alliance with General Electric of the US – including capital exchange dating back a long time before the war – was revived, and so was technological cooperation in 1951. In 1956, Saba was assigned the post of Liaison Engineer between the two companies and transferred to Schenectady, New York. "What I experienced those days was more than useful to me in my subsequent international activities," he said. This was the first of more than 300 trips abroad he would undertake for his company.

The career went successfully on, and the presidency began in 1980, with these words of advice from Saba's presidential predecessor: "It is important for a man of responsibility to have no personal desire in any way."

In 1984, amidst all his work to steer Toshiba in a new direction, Saba received a then-unusual invitation: to join the board of directors of Imperial Chemical Industries (ICI), in the UK. It was here that the final coats of polish were to be applied to his lifelong internationalism.

The seeds of present-day Toshiba were planted, and already had begun to grow.

Then came "The COCOM Incident" of 1987, when he had

been made chairman of the board of Toshiba. Before the collapse of the Soviet Union, industries and governments of the free nations had in effect a compact in which all pledged not to export technology of any military significance to the USSR. Trade relations between Japan and the US in those days were basically delicate, and on top of it there had been background rumblings about firms who were not adhering to the agreement.

Toshiba has and had many dozens of subsidiaries and joint ventures, and one of them, Toshiba Kikai (Toshiba Machine), 51% owned by the parent corporation, got caught filing false export papers and shipping milling machinery to the USSR which could be used to quiet the noise of submarine propellers, making them harder to track on their stealthy missions.

"Because Japan's exports were sweeping over the US market, trade frictions began to emerge in the 1980s between the two countries. In 1986," says Saba, "the US–Japan Semiconductor Agreement was concluded, and the US demanded that its market share within Japan be expanded.

"The incident involving Toshiba Machine Co., Ltd. occurred in the midst of this situation, when Japanese products were conquering the US market and a strong, anti-Japan atmosphere was developing [there].

"Americans regarded Toshiba Kikai as Toshiba, and there was bashing all over the US." In Washington this was unfortunately literally true; some Congresspersons set up a photo opportunity to smash a Toshiba portable tape player to bits on the Capitol lawn. "Children of expatriates [Toshiba workers in the US] were bullied at school. In May a group of radicals came to my house, destroying the garden and painting the word 'traitor' on the wall."[3]

It was a horrible quandary for Toshiba and it seemed irresolvable, because the Japanese administration, warning that the matter of

COCOM violations was a government-to-government affair, ordered the company to do nothing before negotiations were agreed to at that level. The company dangled over a fiery pit.

In April and May Toshiba sent the General Manager of its International Relations Office, Shunsuke Miyao, on more than a dozen trips between Tokyo and Washington, seeking behind-the-scenes advice from Americans on what could be done. "I had been given three sets of advice for Mister Saba: the first was for a high-level Toshiba executive to travel to Washington, DC, and explain in person. The second was to have an outside party conduct a thorough investigation to determine the truth of what happened. The third was [for Toshiba] to institute a much tighter COCOM compliance program."

Back in his office, Saba heard Miyao through to the finish of the 30-minute briefing, and turned his chair slowly to look out on the city. "Yes, yes," he finally said. "I think your report is to the point. When I was in New York a few days ago, after the board meeting of ICI held at the New York Stock Exchange, it was arranged for me to speak privately with the American Secretary of Commerce, Malcolm Baldridge.

"What Mister Baldridge advised me was that it is not a matter between Toshiba and Washington: it is a matter for Washington and Tokyo. It's larger than us. So what he felt I should do is go to the government here in Tokyo and urge them to be more careful about protecting the COCOM covenants."

Saba was quiet for a few more minutes, then spoke again to Miyao. "You know, usually I sleep on the plane back here from New York. But this time I could not close my eyes the whole trip. I thought, 'I'm only a chairman of one private company. How, honestly, can I move the whole government of Japan, or all of the country's industries?' I feel so powerless."

Miyao left Saba's suite with a heavy heart, instinctively sure that he knew what would happen next.

And it did. On 1 July, Saba and Toshiba president Sugiichiro Watari resigned, explaining that they were assuming the blame for the export incident personally.

There was a collective national gasp, in government, business, and among the people, at this extraordinary, almost feudal, gesture. Why, everyone wondered, did Saba, a giant of the industrial community, sacrifice himself for something he had not even done?

"He did the only thing he could," explains Miyao, "after thinking and thinking and thinking, to mobilize the only people who really could resolve the problem, the Japanese government. He did it to put an exclamation point on the seriousness of letting this dispute between Japan and America drag on any longer.

"He himself could do nothing; he had to tell the government and industry that they must be the ones to respond, and quickly. And they did respond: only a few days after that, MITI Minister Tamura himself flew to Washington on this issue – and also Keidanren organized a special committee for coordinating COCOM issues.

"He might have expected this would be the impact of his action. But you know, even in Toshiba he never told the story. So nobody knew why he really did what he did."

NOTES

1. Quoted with permission.
2. "My Personal History," *Nihon Keizai Shimbun*, Tokyo, June 1998
3. "My Personal History."

CHAPTER TEN
PC: PROFITABLE COMPUTERS

It had begun to look like failure again. But Atsutoshi Nishida, standing at the receptionist's desk, knew better. He watched carefully the face of the European sales manager of software giant Lotus Development Corporation, as he crossed the lobby to greet his unwelcome guest. And Nishida saw the painful smile on his face.

"Wonderful!" thought the Toshiba man. "After five visits, this guy's really starting to get tired of me!" He began to sense the deal was about to be closed.

It had to be closed. It was 1985, IBM had introduced the open-system Personal Computer four long years ago,[1] and the PC market train, bound for the whole world, was pulling out of the station already. This was Toshiba's last chance to grab a hand-hold and haul itself aboard.

Toshiba had launched its own desktop computers years before, but it had had neither the engineering expertise nor the marketing structure of its main Japanese competitors Hitachi, Fujitsu, and NEC. And, it had an operating system known to be only about three-quarters compatible with IBM's, which was by then the gold standard in software interoperability. Toshiba had flopped. Worse, it had tried to move that desktop product into the huge American market – and flopped there too.

What was worse than even that for Atsutoshi Nishida was the sickly smell of defeat that hung over the whole idea of trying computers again, back at headquarters in Tokyo. Nishida, engineer Haruhiko Banno, and others had not let go of their faith in computers: after the American loss they had regrouped, considered new approaches, and decided that Toshiba should build a clamshell-cased portable computer. A very small niche – but for that reason leaving all the more room for unopposed entry.

But Toshiba, still smarting from the American humiliation, wasn't at all sure it could feel the same optimism. "You're the last batter up in this game, Nishida-san," the International Operations General Manager told him as he handed across his dispatch papers for Europe in the home office. "Unfortunately I can't give you much money for promotion. So you might as well do whatever you want to do. If you fail, that's it for the computer business."

Worse than having no encouragement to give, Toshiba didn't even have product to give Nishida to sell: in 1983, the first portable PC was still on the drawing boards. When he set down in Europe in 1984, his sample case carried nothing more than proposals.

But that was then. This was the spring of 1985, and Toshiba had shipped him his first few models of the T-1100, a nine-pound package with a 286 Intel processor whose operating system jived perfectly with IBM's, and whose ingenious miniaturization had shrunk the unit to a truly portable state and weight.

Now Nishida's only problem was Toshiba's reputation of non-compatibility with IBM. He knew in fact the new machine was compatible, but he also knew he'd have to prove it.

That's why he was so delightedly annoying the Lotus sales manager.

"Mister Nishida," sighed the executive, settling behind his desk once more, "I can appreciate your problem. You have a very appealing machine. You want to show the world that it runs our very popular retail product Lotus 1-2-3 with the greatest of reliability. But," the executive said gently, "there is this problem we have discussed. Your machine embodies a floppy drive of only 3.5 inches, a brand-new technology that no other computer runs as a standard. If no other computer runs it, Mister Nishida, for us to package 1-2-3 on a 3.5-inch floppy disk would be to take the same gamble you are: that Toshiba will single-handedly convert the computer world to 3.5-inch drives. Frankly almost no one in the computer world believes that."

"But if we could only persuade you," began Nishida. And then he stopped when the sales manager lifted a hand. "Yes. Yes, well, we might be willing, strictly on a good-relations basis, if you will sign the proper patent and sales-agreement documents, to give you an unofficial version in the 3.5 format. Purely for your demonstration purposes."

Deal won.

"So then I went to Ashton-Tate, and talked them into doing the same thing with d-Base III and d-Base IV," recounts Nishida today. "And we were ready to show the product."

Even more persuasion was needed now. "Everyone thought this was just a niche product. And it was expensive, and the screen was black and white, not color. I decided to concentrate on selling to the very biggest firms in Europe, ABB and Royal Dutch-Shell and the ones like that. I told them how ahead of the times our machine was. They complained about the screen. I begged them to look at it for a while: 'You'll get used to it,' I said."

But what really got the portable Toshiba off the ground was its LAN connectivity. "One of the big firms recognized its usefulness, for work done outside the office as well as inside, and gave us an order for 100 units! So then I could go back to all those other companies again, and tell them I had made the sale – and they all took a second, harder look at it. And it began to sell."

It wasn't just a matter of convincing data managers, Nishida readily admits. He had to work hard getting lunch and dinner appointments with key procurement executives, and then charming them with long, civilized discussions of comparative cultures – a thing easy enough to do, since he himself was a university graduate in the history of Western political thought. "In France I talked about Montesquieu, in Germany about Edmund Husserl. The important thing, I knew, was to build a relationship, to build trust, with these executives. Because not only would there be a first sale, but a second and a third after that."

And soon he was sending a message to Tokyo, asking them to ramp up for 10,000 computers in the first year. Tokyo was shocked. Even more shocked when it had to ramp up for 20,000 machines the next year.

The portable PC had made it beyond the realm of footnote.

The world might have been a stranger to Toshiba's computers, but Toshiba was no newcomer, even with its desktop, to the computer business. As long ago as 1958 it had formed a partnership with Sperry Rand and a trading company, Daiichi Bussan, specifically to sell UNIVAC machines in the Japan market.[2]

In the 1960s and 1970s a different kind of market stimulus – the corporate presence of IBM in Japan – stirred the Ministry of International Trade and Industry (MITI) to organize Japan's largest electrical-electronics firms (Fujitsu, Hitachi, NEC, Toshiba, Mitsubishi Electric, Oki Electric) as impromptu R&D and product-development groups, to try to compete against the American giant. Japan was very much afraid, at the time, that IBM would quickly overwhelm any domestic competitors and capture almost the entirety of the Japanese market, just then awakening to the era of computerization.

Tough negotiations directly between MITI and IBM produced agreements to allow the latter to enter Japan, and soon to manufacture there, but only at the stipulation that IBM would open its patents to any Japanese firm desiring them, at very favorable royalty rates. Thus the Japanese companies brought together by MITI could enter the race with a strong advantage: they could build computers compatible with IBM's systems, and the government would finance majority percentages of the research costs needed to build Japanese computers.

The work was scrupulously organized and Toshiba, with its technological agreements with GE, was paired with NEC and that firm's overseas partner Honeywell. As a result, "Combined, the alliance had 20% of the [Japanese] computer market," observes one study of the unfolding race.[3] But "Toshiba's models did not sell well, and, by the 1980s, Toshiba, no longer willing to bear the high cost of producing mainframe computers . . . decided to drop out . . . and funneled its own efforts into small business computers and minicomputers."

This is where its decision has moved it today: No. 1 in the world, for seven straight years, in portable machines.

But also, the experience gained in national products, it has been pointed out, launched several other enduring lines of business. In another MITI-sponsored and -financed research project, the Pattern Information Processing Project of 1971–80, Toshiba's role evolved into refining the computerized character recognition (see Chapter 7) used in the letter-sorting machines that Toshiba already made for the Post Office, as well as counterfeit-currency detection machines and, later, voice-recognition technology that, among other things, interfaces with bank customers via telephone to report balances to them automatically, and interacts with motorists via car-navigation equipment to help them reach their destinations faster.

Nishida, meanwhile, let no grass grow beneath his feet. In 1986, "Since we were rather successful in introducing the first [port-

Hisashige Tanaka (1799–1881), the
'Edison of Japan,' founded the
Tanaka Engineering Works, fore-
runner of today's Toshiba, in 1875.

A 1904 woodblock print of Shibaura Engineering Works Co., Ltd. Toshiba's 39-story headquarters building now stands near the same spot on Tokyo Bay.

Japan's first electric washing machine, introduced by Toshiba in 1930. The company is still one of Japan's leaders in home appliances.

The Toshiba electric rice cooker, launched in 1955 and a fixture in every second Japanese household within a few years.

Philip Reed (*right*), chairman of General Electric, joins Taizo Ishizaka (*left*), then president of Toshiba, and Kiyoshi Ishikawa, a director of Toshiba, for a tour of Tsurumi Works during his 1955 visit to Japan. GE had a long capital relationship with Toshiba and remains an important partner in several areas.

In 1955, as Toshiba reinvented itself as a modern mass-manufacturer, the company's then-president, Taizo Ishizaka (*left*), led a delegation from the Japan Productivity Center to the US. Here he returns to Japan, along with Kiichiro Sato (*middle*), president of Mitsui Bank, and Naokazu Ishiguro, Toshiba's general manager for external affairs.

Concerned that concentration of power in Tokyo could be a problem, Toshio Doko, president of Toshiba (1965–73), made frequent and unannounced visits to production sites to see things from the perspective of local management. Here he visits a heavy machinery plant.

Fukaya Works gears up for color TV production in 1965. A pioneer in the Japanese market, Toshiba remains a leader in the world market for color TVs.

A young Dr Kenichi Mori in 1967, ready to turn over the world's first automatic Japanese mail-sorting machine to the post office. He refined the technology used in this equipment to create the Japanese-language word processor in 1978, another world first.

Toshiba Science Institute invites the public – especially kids – to explore electronics and Toshiba's achievements and latest advances. Exhibits include the world's largest incandescent light bulb, almost a meter high – and the smallest, only a fourth the size of a grain of rice.

able] machine in Europe, I was sure of our future success so we decided to transfer this business to the USA." Toshiba kept producing more and more refined versions, especially of the viewscreens, and an American vindication at last ensued: "In 1991–92 we became No. 1 in the country over Compaq."

It was a short-lived victory. Compaq, one of the most influential of portable PC makers who had sprung up in the US, went to war against Toshiba on the price front, slashing its list prices severely and encroaching swiftly on Toshiba's position. This battle resulted in Compaq's seizing the No. 1 spot in 1993.

Nishida had by then long since returned to Tokyo to head up overseas personal-computer operations – but found himself reposted in 1992 to the presidency of Toshiba America Information Systems. He visited the US, then returned to confront the board with a troublesome analysis. Toshiba had been caught by the Compaq maneuver with a big back inventory, and the only way to clear it would be to counter-cut costs of the Toshiba portable PC.

"I requested our executives to please accept that what I was thinking was in the range of 56 million dollars in cuts. They were shocked: 'Do you understand how much money you are talking about?' they asked me. 'Yessir,' I said. 'Fifty-six million dollars in price cuts – that's what we need!' They couldn't understand it, of course. 'In the history of the corporation we've never cut prices to that extent,' they said. 'Well, it's a managerial decision,' I told them. 'I'm a salaryman – I just work for you!'

"Three days later they sent me back, we made the cuts, and we had to go back to work all over again." But it wasn't only sad news he took with him to Irvine, California. Under his arm he had tucked a completely new product, with an Intel 486 processor and a full-color thin-film-transistor display screen of startling clarity. Portable PCs had always been thought, of course, inferior in performance to desktop computers because of their size. "But now, Toshiba was cracking that barrier – and this was a very powerful machine to be carrying around in your hand.

"I couldn't get the sales team to understand the concept at first. They said, 'It's too expensive! Fifty percent higher than Compaq!' But I said, 'It's not a Compaq. Come with me and watch.'"

And he took the salesmen for a bit of on-the-job training. "I took the machine to five or six information services managers in big companies. I showed them the color screen, and I asked them, 'Tell me, do you believe that portable PC screens will still be black and white next year?' And they said of course, no. And I showed them the computer speed and power of the 486 chip and I asked them, 'Tell me, do you think portable PCs will still be running 386 chips next year?' And they all said no. And I asked, 'How many years in your depreciation accounting schedule?' And the answer was three. And it was obvious they could have the best machine right now, and depreciate it a year earlier than if they waited for some other maker's model to come out next year. Its cost performance really came out much better.

"So our salesmen started using that argument with their customers, and our sales of course went back up."

There were other tactics Nishida had up his sleeve: or at least in one case, up his cuff. He took his top sales managers to visit the main offices in California of a large sports-shoe maker, preparing for the sales call the next day. He wanted to get a taste of the customer's corporate culture.

On the ground floor, he wandered entranced among racks and racks of shoes. By the time his colleagues relocated him, he was wearing a flashy pair of black-and-white high-tops. They applauded him. "Yes," Nishida said. "I'm going to buy these. In fact, we all are."

And so, when the formal sales presentation call was made the next morning, the Toshiba executive team trooped in wearing their Italian-cut business suits, each finished off at the feet in a pair of the client's flashy footwear. The tactic worked.

So did another tactic used with a major airline that was driving unusually hard for a discount on a big order of portable PCs that Nishida just could not afford to give. "OK," he said at last. "You can have your discount – if you give us the difference back in airline tickets, for our business travel!" They gave, and Nishida got that contract too.

There was strategic work that wasn't much fun – hard bargaining with large-scale computer retail outlets, as the Toshiba portable PCs began to catch on with the computing public. Some dealers commanding big shelf space demanded a 25% price cut. "That was all of our profits – we couldn't give it! So we just excused ourselves politely and left. Then CompUSA, one of the big ones, agreed to a 15% margin. We signed. The other dealers began calling us back, to restart negotiations. And by 1994 we had regained No. 1 share in the United States, and kept it for five straight years. In the same year we also arrived at No. 1 globally in portable computers – and we haven't lost it since."

There was, though, more to this Toshiba success than just the flair and bravado of sales wizards like Nishida, who is now company president and CEO of Toshiba's Digital Media Network Co., which handles computers and many other things besides.

There is the lucky fact that the instincts of Nishida and engineering colleague Banno were right for the moment: portable PCs and other forms of portable machines made up only 2% of the global computer market at the time Toshiba reentered it with its diminutive new products. That share has now grown to 20% globally – and to 57% in Japan, where desk space for office equipment is precious. And it continues to climb everywhere.

As portable PCs add power and performance to equal or

outshine desktop machines, the natural replacement cycle of the latter, three to four years, will almost automatically bring about a shift in demand to the more convenient and mobile little machines, and so drive that share higher.

In other words, Toshiba operates in a sector of the PC market that still holds great growth promise, and at very good margins. In fact, in retrospect the company was lucky to be late.

And it isn't just the machines themselves that make margins. It's the fact that Toshiba, when its competitors have long switched to the integrator model of manufacturing, securing all or almost all of their parts from other suppliers, still makes so many of the highest-value-added components of the portable PC itself.

It's the corporation's constant investment in technology that has allowed Toshiba to follow its "Voice of the Customer" strategy, by answering market calls for lightness, performance versatility, communications abilities, power, speed, and mobility in its own factories. Toshiba was first to develop a lithium-ion battery for PC use to gain longer operating times. Lithium ion gives twice the length of powering time of the old nickel-metal hydride cells for portable computers. The hard-disk drives, the 2.5-inch models that store 40 gigabytes, were thought up and realized in Toshiba's R&D center.

Then there are the low-temperature polysilicon TFT liquid crystal displays, with switching that is up to 100 times as fast as the old, amorphous LCDs, meaning that movies can be shown with much greater definition for the digital images from the built-in optical DVD disk drive that Toshiba developed – all of these contribute something extra to the profit line from a product that sold 3.7 million units last year.

"No no," says Haruhiko Banno, father of Toshiba's portable PC and now Chief Technology Executive of the Digital Media Network Co. "We're not afraid of the competition. Because they almost can't do what we can do. Yes, we can make longer-life batteries, and lighter carry weights with magnesium or titanium cases.

"But think of television technology – more particularly, digital television! We can put that in our computers. What other portable PC maker has the in-house capability to design and produce LSIs that can bring digital television to a portable PC screen? And now we've entered the broadband era for telecommunications. NTT DoCoMo mobile phones have already introduced the W-CDMA technology – and we make those types of telephone terminals right now. So already we are at work on the convergence between CDMA cellular communication and personal computers.

"We have the technology to develop these very advanced machines. And no one else does."

A more thoughtful look behind these words shows the true master product strategy of Toshiba at work. It is here in personal computers that the corporation's profound faith – that it can upset routine market wisdom and bend competitive outcomes to its own ends on a global scale by dipping into its ever-replenished cornucopia of technologies – is most plainly revealed. What seems ultimately destined to become for all competitors just another thin-margin, or no-margin, commodity product once saturation is complete, is really an eternally open doorway to an ever richer market for the skills of Toshiba.

"Compared to desktop computers," Nishida explains, "we can use such abilities as nanotechnology to go on expanding the product concept. In that sense technological development of the portable PC will be infinite! It can be the core of a home network system: include Bluetooth or other wireless network capability, linking it to a small server in the home itself, and connect the proper interfaces, and it can incorporate control of almost anything in the house, or connected to the house: satellite down-links, mobile phones, digital TVs and optical disk movies and appliances and on and on. And most of this would be invisible to the user!"

Toshiba bets on adding something new and something better than the competition, at every turn of the market, almost forever. Portable PCs, as a central locus of all these new capabilities, are a product that for Toshiba can never fall to the fatal category of "commodities."

But the product cycle, no matter how glitzy or how accelerated, is not the whole truth of marketing competition, of course. In an environment confused with so many competitors and customers who, like Mister Nishida's so many years before in Europe, have a hard time telling real and useful breakthroughs from the niches of "bells and whistles," does Toshiba have an infinite supply of young Nishidas to explain it all and close the sale?

In a boardroom five thousand miles from the product-development computer screens, in Irvine, California, President Hisatsugu Nonaka of Toshiba America Information Systems, the executive heir to Nishida, sifts the clues of *his* marketplace, the USA, and strains to hear the Voice of the Customer each day.

Every three months Nonaka flies back to a product-planning seminar in Tokyo to input what he's learned into the engineering mix. And the engineers listen intently, because they know that they must know what the buyer wants them to make.

"It used to be that customers only knew portable PCs for their small size. But now they are learning constantly, and they are becoming more and more demanding in every aspect," says Nonaka. "And not just regarding the product itself: they want faster delivery times, higher quality levels, quicker service guarantees, better image-loading on their sets."

He is speaking of his corporate customers, the area where Toshiba is strong in the American market. Nonaka has inherited from past marketing successes a stable of perhaps 300 major clients, such as Oracle, Sprint, and Deloitte & Touche. And he's learned how to serve them well to keep their business.

"We can furnish multiple operating systems for given work environments," ticks off Nonaka's General Manager for Sales and Service, Mark Simons. "We can convert them from one Windows operating system generation to the next, bringing along all their applications by supplying them in next-generation Toshiba portable PCs, by leasing them new machines, or by distributing software, whatever their price range and desires. We can even convert their existing machines to new software sets over the phone!"

But Nonaka, who commands 12 to 13% of the portable PC market in America, has now begun to see new marketing horizons. "Dell and other guys have strong desktop and portable PC and other businesses. But they're all PC guys really, not mobile guys. They don't focus on mobile solutions for the customers. And since we're so strong in wireless technology, we do. And you know, we can see a humongous market for the future in this mobile area."

Nonaka is concentrating on how to sell mobile capabilities as a part of, not a separate system that attaches to, computers. "The corporate people don't need just hardware anymore, and they know that's what they're being sold. They are getting harder and harder in their demands for price cuts.

"But are computers what they really need? No. They really need solutions. Servers are the key to solutions. Our server business is growing a little bit, but I'm frustrated with it. It could grow a lot faster. Look, if you know that big companies have discovered the value of the server system, how far behind can the mid-size and little companies be? You can sell a PC-and-server system to a neighborhood insurance agency, if you can show them how to use it to make money, and give it to them at a reasonable price!"

Networks of this sort, and the key they represent to computer makers for lifelong business with big clients, have long been a hot competitive market. IBM is the market leader, almost twice as large as No. 2 Electronic Data Systems. The merger announcement between Compaq and Hewlett-Packard in mid 2001 was made at least as much with the service-expansion idea in mind as to create the United States' second-largest PC maker.

"We have to get to them [the smaller and medium-sized customers] quickly, while the desktop-replacement market is hot, to show them this extra dimension of Toshiba as a solutions provider," says Nonaka of his own strategic target. "We've reorganized our sales: we are expanding our direct contacts with business customers. We've fine-tuned this so much that on most configure-to-order purchases for corporate customers, we can deliver the product in just 48 hours."

But what about consumers, another important part of the customer equation? Two US competitors sell by direct marketing, Dell and Gateway, using expensive television advertising. What about Toshiba?

"We've extended our own direct marketing, mail-order and catalog programs, and added an Internet campaign called 'Shop Toshiba.' It's getting good results. We also have all our old chains through the major discount retailers, and though the margins are being squeezed, we've learned one curious thing. Once we introduce a new product with new features to the business customer, within a couple of months the word spreads among consumers – and they will buy it, even at premium price, just because they want it! Just in July, one of CompUSA's best-selling portable PCs was our most expensive box, with the combination drive [that both plays and rewrites DVDs] built in.

"And when the next-generation computer shows up, including wireless Internet access and its own personal digital assistant functions, a pager and a movie player and so on," adds Simons, "we think consumers will be entranced all over again."

Mobile network systems for business customers; notebook movies and instant Internet connections for consumers . . . Will they be entranced?

It's at least partly, again, a question of the all-important speed to market. And Nonaka is already in possession of the answer. In September 2001 Toshiba America Information Systems announced on the US market its newest-generation portable PC, with flash memory-card slots, DVD multi-function drives, mammoth-capacity hard-disk memories, weights as low as 4.4 lbs. – and built-in antennas for both Bluetooth and other wireless communication systems.

Technology fully loaded, the future is already here.

NOTES

1. "It was 20 years ago today . . .", *InfoWorld*, California, 6 August 2001
2. Marie Anchordoguy, *Computers Inc.: Japan's Challenge to IBM*, Council on East Asian Studies, Harvard University, 1989. Much of this discussion of Toshiba's development history in computers is taken from this source.
3. Ibid.

CHAPTER ELEVEN
ENGRAVED ON SILICON:
THE BOTTOM LINE

It was the best of times, it was the worst of times.

Even so, some days are better than others.

It was a great day, for example, when Masahide Ohashi pushed the doorbell, figuratively speaking, of Ken Kutaragi at Sony, and showed him a product that had been already four years in the making, with no buyers anywhere in sight.

Kutaragi liked what he saw. He ended up buying it. And made Toshiba a good deal richer.

Everybody knows about video games. Depending on the game you choose, they can be fiendishly hard to outwit. But few players know how very, very hard it is to put together a game machine containing the microchips that do all of that: run the game program, create all the pictures and activate them into motion, keep score, declare winners and losers. Designing and building those semiconductors is fiendishly hard, too.

The story of the Toshiba–Sony partnership, beginning with Sony's PlayStation 1, today morphed into PlayStation 2, begins with Ohashi and colleague Mitsuo Saito, both of that part of the Toshiba Corporation which would become Toshiba Semiconductor Co., fooling around in early 1986 with an idea for a product. Ohashi was a graphics man, and lived what seemed to be the right kind of life for one: sky-diving, motorcycles, non-stop action. Saito was a microprocessor man, and contented himself with bicycling.

But Saito, thanks to a Toshiba corporate contribution to MIT's Media Lab, had been invited for a sabbatical there, and had seen the wonders of visual media welling up out of MIT's genius. He was impressed.

The two men were friends. When Saito got back home they decided, just for the fun of it, to develop Toshiba's first experimental graphics chip. Geometry transformation was the key; each picture was broken down by computer into thousands and thousands of tiny polygons, and then each polygon was filled with the appropriate color to reconstitute the two-dimensional polygons into a full spread that appeared on the screen to be one big, three-dimensional image.

Then they finished, and not knowing what else to do with it, they put the chip back on the shelf and returned to real work.

But Ohashi, of course, didn't forget about it.

He took it to a technical fair in Silicon Valley, where engineers of NEXT Computer Co. took an immediate interest in it, as a possibly inexpensive way to incorporate graphics in PC programs (graphics technologies that existed then were expensive, and confined largely to big and powerful workstation machines for design jobs). The NEXT team aimed at something between a workstation and a PC, using Ohashi's chip – but the project flopped.

Many other companies that had seen the chip tried, in succession, to commercialize it in various products – but all failed. Still, the general interest provided room enough in Toshiba Semiconductor's budget to keep working at the chip, polishing it and repolishing it.

Then came Ohashi's visit to Kutaragi, who quickly reciprocated with a visit of his own to Toshiba, to ask if they would develop the graphics device for a new line of Sony video games Kutaragi wanted to build. History began on that day.

Kutaragi said he thought he could sell two million of the game machines, and was willing to let Toshiba make as well as design the chips. The two companies settled on a price of about two thousand yen per piece, which even if Sony managed to sell only half its forecast, would work out to two billion yen for Toshiba. PlayStation 1, seven years after its 1994 launch, was still selling one million units per month.

But with the basic technology mastered, it appeared both to Sony and Toshiba that the product could be vastly improved, and a second-generation PlayStation would be devised that promised sparkling color, brilliant definition, and most important, smooth, natural motion, at both high speeds and those subtly slow.

Toshiba and Sony Computer Entertainment signed a joint venture and launched the quest for PS2. This would take video games to the next level, one richer and more realistic. It would require a graphics chip that could render movie-quality images and a microprocessor with the power to control all aspects of operation – including taking those images and displaying them at an unprecedented rate. Achieving that would require a CPU with calculation performance matching that of a super computer. And Toshiba would develop it.

As the microprocessor project began, tragedy dealt a mean joker into the game. Masahide Ohashi died of cancer in early 1996. Heartsick, Saito had to marshal a new management team to soldier on with the design and development. It took a lot of soldiering: Toshiba divided its design efforts between Tokyo and its Silicon Valley lab, and eventually 150 engineers from both sides of the Pacific were at work on the project. As one section changed its design, any number of others had to be made aware of it so they could change theirs to fit.

Weeks turned into months and then into years. The engineers reached for unprecedented goals and the media speculated as to whether or not they were possible. The world's fastest 128-bit microprocessor, able to perform at a staggering 6.2 gigaflops. Capable of rebuilding 3D graphics at a peak rate of 66 million polygons a second, with perfect perspective and realistic curved surfaces. And manufacturable: a "computer on a chip" that could be produced, with high yields, at Toshiba's Oita Operations.

In 1999 it was all done, all doubts pushed aside. PlayStation 2 bowed onto Sony's stage and hasn't left the spotlight yet. The Oita production line, itself a joint venture between the two partners, now rolls off 1.5 million per month of the chip that performs so closely to its targets it has been named "The Emotion Engine." It's the heart of a machine that can generate excitement, sorrow, pride, and other human responses among its users, using just micro-size electrical impulses.

Other feelings flew on the wings of PS2, also. The Sunday after the new product was announced, Mitsuo Saito visited Ohashi's widow and their two children at home, to open the box and set up their new PlayStation 2, and show them how to use it.

PS2 should sell, making big profits for Toshiba without any user actually even realizing it's run by a Toshiba computer-on-a-chip, for many years. It's a global product.

But it's not Ohashi's only legacy. Since its completion, Toshiba, Sony Computer Entertainment – and now IBM – have come to see incipient promise in the basic design of the micro-controller, for use in multimedia circuitry. So much promise that they have negotiated a new, three-way joint venture to develop together the next stage of the Emotion Engine, a one-teraflop central processing unit (roughly 160 times faster than the Emotion Engine's controller) that will dovetail exquisitely with the broadband age.

Saito is the project leader from Toshiba Semiconductor, and he admits that just about all of his engineers are now focused on the project, code-named CELL. "Right now the total budget for CELL is about 400 million dollars," he says, and he freely admits it's all a gamble. "I cannot even imagine what kind of application a software writer could use with all this power. It's really a bet, a very big bet. If we're not successful, we'll take a big hit to our investment."

He probably shouldn't worry. Somewhere out there, in Toshiba Semiconductors, in Sony Computer Entertainment or in IBM, there's likely a new Masahide Ohashi, ready to take the finished invention out and show the world what it can do.

Even so, there is another, perhaps still more important legacy of his work for Toshiba – a sort of grandson chip to the Emotion Engine, which we shall visit below.

If some days are better than others, the most recent ones have not been good for Takeshi Nakagawa, president of Toshiba Semiconductor Co. "This is the toughest year in my career," he summarizes simply.

That might sound surprising, coming from the head of a microchip empire that is No. 2 in the world, behind Intel, counting all the Integrated Circuit (IC) product families that Toshiba makes. Nakagawa has been a Toshiba man for 37 years, and that surely must take in some bad times in the past. Why are these the worst?

"Speed. Speed and sharpness of the demand cycles – swift upturns and deep downturns. We are now within the shortest of cycles between the two I can ever remember. They used to run, famously, for four years each. Everybody knew it. It was called the silicon cycle; typically the bottom of the downturn coincided with each Olympic year, for some reason. But now? Who knows – now it may be down to three years, to two years. No one knows."

Other kinds of memories are hurting Nakagawa too. Memory

chips. Toshiba has gone from being the largest merchant DRAM maker in the world, in the late 1980s, to 6 to 8% of the market in mid 2001, as simple DRAMs turned into the worst-hurt victims of the entire decline of the information technology field in the new century. DRAMs, as I spoke to Nakagawa in the summer of 2001, had been crushed down drastically from their former open-market prices, and still the bottom was not in sight. With Toshiba's production capacity at 25 million units per month, the situation obviously could not hold.

In August, Toshiba announced the closing of half its production capacity at its Yokkaichi DRAM Operations plant, cutting capacity in a single stroke from 25 to 20 million chips per month.

Nakagawa knows that more could follow. It isn't that his company will be wiped out – it's just that DRAMs, once the pride of Toshiba's semiconductor fleet, used to produce a major part of the stream of cash that funded R&D for the corporation itself. As Toshiba's then-president Taizo Nishimuro himself put it, "Nothing will replace the profits we once generated from chips."[1]

And it all happened less than a year after Toshiba had drawn up a budget for 170 billion yen more investment in the chip business, so promising had the future for IT looked back in mid 2000.[2]

Of course this cycle downturn hurt all of Toshiba's competitors too, those with cost advantages and those without. But a bit of perspective on just how it has damaged the world's No. 2 semiconductor manufacturer is instructive.

Toshiba grew so large as a merchant chip seller – that is, one who manufactures to industry-standard specifications, and sells to customers all over the world – because it planned to be. Toshiba uses memories of course in many of its own products.

And once its very high-quality fabrication plants were erected, turning out an excess for other customers who use chips but have no "fabs" was simple. (All this was just as obvious to Toshiba's Japanese competitors, so that C.H. Ferguson and C.R. Morris were able to remark as early as 1993, "While the Japanese control less than a quarter of the (world) computer industry, they make well over half its components."[3])

And it got, in fact, much simpler in the latter part of the 1980s, when the Japan Land Bubble, a speculative maelstrom that infected the entire national economy, permitted companies like Toshiba to raise capital very easily in the stock and other securities markets, and to borrow huge sums outright from its main banks. It was this cash, invested in chip plants, that allowed Toshiba to leverage itself to world's overall No. 1.

But there were complications implicit in this market-grabbing strategy for memories. As Martin Fransman asked in 1995, "Why are Japanese companies globally dominant in memory semi-conductors, but hold only a minute fraction of the world market for microprocessors which use the same process technology as memories?"[4] Certainly Toshiba was capable of making its own microprocessors, and one might say it had a special interest in doing so, with its obvious dominance of the portable computer market.

That, at least in Toshiba's case, is the answer as well as the question. Toshiba had need for microprocessors only in the computer line (cell phones were not a large product line for Toshiba then). But by the time it grew into its portable PC predominance, the major "owners" of the personal computer technology-standards space were Intel for hardware, and Micro-soft for software. Together they had symbiotic products that dominated the industry, because of the huge sphere of applications software that would run on Microsoft operating systems and Intel central processing units. No one would pay the extra money a Toshiba-designed and built CPU would cost, if the only thing it did was run what Intel chips already ran.

So Toshiba had no compulsion to do other than buy Intel "hearts" for its own personal computers.

However in relying on memory chips as the company's biggest money-maker (at one time, the merchant business brought in some 70% of all of Toshiba Corporation's annual profits), Toshiba acquired an interest in seeing that standards of performance and application for memories *never changed*. That would have demanded redesign and retooling, which would have destroyed the Toshiba profits base.

So, in effect, Toshiba and other Japanese makers were retarding the technological development of the standard memory chip – to the point that Korean and Taiwanese chipmakers were eventually able to catch up to them in building their own factories, and in turning out quality chips while underpricing the Japanese by 50%.

The main plan for recoupment of position and losses is developmental. New memories, both volatile and non-volatile, have been created or developed by Toshiba and are already in production. Their performance is better, their price is higher, the demand is likely to recover and grow fastest. There's a FeRAM, that is expected to be used in mobile phones. FeRAM can read data faster by adopting random access memory and retain data when power is off. Toshiba has already developed an 8-megabit version which is to be developed into a 32-megabit version.

And "actually, we have quite a good position in Rambus memory devices," adds Corporate Senior Executive Vice President Yasuo Morimoto. "Only two other companies beside us can supply them. They're not easy to design into an LSI, because they are quite sensitive. But if done properly, it can speed up your machine's functions considerably. It's for use in both personal computers and computer games, two very large markets."

There's a non-volatile memory called NOR, which will be in huge demand once 3G cell phones take off.

And then of course there's the NAND flash memory, which Toshiba invented, now manufactures at its Yokkaichi Operations, and turns out in the form of two industry-leading memory cards. One is the SmartMedia Card, a Toshiba-developed format now supported by almost 200 companies: it is about the size of a postage stamp and widely used in digital cameras. The latest version can store over 1,000 digital still images, and is of course reusable. Second is the SD Memory Card, co-developed with industry giants Matsushita (Panasonic) and SanDisk of the US, an even smaller, smarter form of flash memory card that is security protected, an advantage that has already attracted over 400 companies to the SD Association.

The automatic protection engineered into the SD Memory Card, to guard against unauthorized copying, makes it a versatile new type of recording medium for devices such as MP3 music players. It is this chip that Toshiba hopes to marry to both Internet and mobile phone technology, so that consumers can dial up the music they want, and download it onto flash memory chips as the recording medium. Once popularized, this chip could virtually replace disks for musical storage, and dozens of chips could fit into a single pocket.

This tiny flash memory, thinks Yoshihiro Nitta, Executive Vice President of Digital Media Network Co., presents fascinating business possibilities. The memory, now capable of storing 512 megabytes, will be produced in one-gigabyte capacities by next year. "That's more than the capacity of a CD, a full CD music disk."

If music distributors see that a performance downloaded to an SD Memory Card cannot be recopied at all, Nitta believes, they will be ready to sell performances over cell-phone connections that can be listened to at any time, recorded once, but never re-copied.

And some day, you'll be able to visit the music store and purchase an entire opera recorded on a medium not much broader than your thumb.

As NAND memories quickly move toward this kind of application, their presence is spreading and so is demand. The SD Memory Card looks as though it may become the de facto standard for the industry, but even if it doesn't – if, for example, Sony's Memory Stick flash memory medium emerges as the winner – NAND memories everywhere will still incorporate a core chip on which Toshiba receives a royalty.

Predictably, the flash memory has yet another strategic role to play for Toshiba. "As a component, part of the attractiveness to us of these products is a secondary feedback – we put them in Toshiba products, and Toshiba is known for its quality largely because of them, though the customers may never know or see them. But our competitors know it is in there, and we can generate demand from them to use our parts in their own product, so they can offer the same product quality under their own brands."

In other words, memory marketing in the future, as a merchant product, is fully intended to work out as memorably as did DRAMs.

Toshiba is completely, if somewhat ruefully, aware, of course of the industrial Darwinism of high technology and how perilous it can be to become the largest of enterprises dealing in it – a somewhat painful fact for a Japanese industrial giant, with decades of government protectionism and guidance, if not outright subsidy, formerly cushioning it.

Critics point out there is danger ahead for a Toshiba who

insists on manufacturing, or at least developing to the manufacturing point, everything for itself, by itself. The capital risk grows exponentially.

But in reality it seldom works exactly that way.

An example, from the semiconductor side of Toshiba, of how the company acquires the best of technologies while lowering its risk profile to acceptable curves comes from the fact that Toshiba not only designs its own semiconductor-manufacturing technology, just to make sure the right tools are at hand when needed, but it no longer tries to do that on its own. It has partnerships.

This spring, for example, Toshiba and Sony Corp. announced a joint research & development project to perfect design technology for manufacturing large-scale integrated circuits with line widths of just 0.07 microns. The techniques, which when perfected will be called CMOS 5, will likely be used by Toshiba to build its CELL System on a Chip, because generally the narrower the lines engraved on a semiconductor, the faster it operates.

But CMOS 5 – and 6, and 7, which will undoubtedly grow out of it – will be a possession of Toshiba and can be used for any part of semiconductor technology it wants. The main point is, it will get this enormously valuable tool at only half-price.

"This is going to run 125 million dollars, split between us and Sony equally," says Katsuji Fujita, Semiconductor Company vice-president. "If we had to pay that much money by ourselves, the path would quickly lead to bankruptcy. And there are a lot of those-size projects in the future for us."

But where will the profits to repay even that hedged investment come from?

From the large-scale integrations, like the Emotion Engine, that the technology will build. Toshiba is going to skip over the whole, lost generation of central processing units, and rush quickly into the system-on-a-chip future. "For Toshiba micro-processors, the personal computer market is over," is the way Semiconductor Company president Nakagawa puts it. "The cell-phone handset market is over.

"So we are going to prioritize the so-called digital home market."

And that means what?

"We can use LSIs [large-scale integrated circuits, as systems-on-a-chip are called] for home wireless applications of all sorts. Imagine wireless audio and TV and recording for both, wireless Internet and computer linkages to it without wires. Wires are going to disappear from your home in a few years! Products like digital TV, digital still camera, satellite downlink, cable TV and telephone, all the information from them will be inserted into a wireless server and stored there. That market will likely be huge.

"A new era is coming for silicon now. If you make the technology, and make the products, and get people to buy them – you're building the industry yourself."

With 150 engineers from two major corporations working on it over a period of years, you could say the Emotion Engine was something of a milestone for Toshiba. The payoff has long been flowing in, not only to the company's coffers but to its treasury of technologies that can be built upon as foundations of the future.

The 400-million-dollar joint venture project to build a next-generation CELL chip, 160 times faster than the Emotion Engine, is not the only direction in which Toshiba is steering this compiled experience in LSI-making.

In a grassy business-park campus in Silicon Valley there is a building housing offices and design shops that belong to Toshiba America Electronic Components, Inc. And inside that building is a small, quiet, white-walled lab, sealed off almost as securely as a defense installation – from the rest of its Toshiba fellows.

It's sealed off not so much for security as for the reason that it is a completely separate subsidiary, ArTile Microsystems Inc., and its job is to work minor miracles with the major piece of work called the Emotion Engine.

Silicon Valley has changed, in at least two ways. The landscape of electronic genius is now composed not so much of giant, know-it-all and do-it-all semiconductor makers as it is of small, specialized companies that more and more follow the changing pattern of the *market* for chips, which is the second change to come to the valley.

"There is a lot of growing demand here now for the system on a chip," explains Tomohisa Shigematsu, chief executive officer of ArTile. As silicon technology is more and more miniaturized, "The next page in history is the scale of the chips. Think of ten million logic gates on a chip – maybe it will be even more than that."

And the rest of the system on that chip, besides the microprocessor, are the memories, the connecting buses, the graphics chips and communications chips, and all the peripheral chips that produce the system's product, whether it be a moving image on a flat-panel display or a routing director for a multimedia server unit.

In other words an SOC's got to be, whatever else it is, a big concept in a very small space. And that is where the Emotion Engine entered the scene.

"In March 1999 we knew we had the challenge, now that the Emotion Engine project was finished," says Shardul Kazi, chief operating officer of ArTile, of how to take the sophisticated design and change it from games to a general-purpose microprocessor, "so that we can target the technology on other market segments as well."

They decided those segments would be multimedia devices, set-top boxes, networking routers, and the like. And by 2000 they had their modification finished and ready to go: the TX79 microprocessor.

The TX79 can be sold in simple, off-the-shelf system chips, for average applications. Or it can – and this is the big promise of cash return – be customized for a single client's applications. Pixelworks, Inc., a solution-based provider of video, computer graphics, and Web information displays used in both business and consumer markets, gave ArTile an eight-figure contract to create its next-generation SOC, code-named JOLT.

ArTile's work here was a six-month job, more or less at the extreme of the type of assignments it accepts. But it illustrates the type of work the wholly owned Toshiba subsidiary is capable of doing. This exotic SOC begins with the TX79 microprocessor, its brain. Then Pixelworks' own chip design containing its proprietary circuitry is turned over to ArTile for incorporation. Then other chips, to accomplish all the applications, must be found and melded in, along with suitable memories and interconnections.

Other chips? IPs, they are called in the industry – and they are another example of the fragmentation of the business in Silicon Valley. Certain companies deal only in the designs of routine, or exotic, application chips. These firms keep files of designs on hand and when a company like ArTile comes calling for the right type of IP (for intellectual property, or patent) to do a certain job, it sells or leases them the license.

ArTile brings all the pieces together and then uses chip-design tools to connect them. But time is of the essence in its business, and so it uses a special technology to cut the integration times down from weeks to days. And that precisely is the secret to ArTile's success: it divides the total of the designs into related blocs, called tiles (thus the company's name), each of whose design can be worked out on computers simultaneously – five, six, eight design jobs, very complex, all going on at once.

And then, all brought back together when each is finished, fitted onto the single chip, and readied for production in a fabrication plant. SOCs of this sort are so complicated that Artile adds a special testing circuitry built into the chip itself, so that specific functions can be automatically tested when manufacture is finished, just by hooking the circuit to a test-machine computer. In a sense, the chip diagnoses itself, saving much time and expense over routine testing methods.

What does all of this mean? It implies something that the ArTile people have thought long and hard about. Toshiba must now "migrate," as business language has it, to LSIs, the upper end of the chip business. LSIs are more and more being sought from suppliers in the finished form of SOCs, in other words slightly or highly sophisticated custom designs. "Probably more than 60% of our business is doing custom chips, one chip for one customer. It cannot be given to any other customer, as a condition of the order," says Shigematsu.

Margins are quite good for this work, if you can provide the speed and the faultless automation of computer design tools like the ArTile technology itself.

But – the market has an exactly opposite character to that of the old memory-chip business. With standard products, a corporation like Toshiba could build its lines and turn out identical products for similar uses by the millions. Cost could be cut greatly by the mere scale of production achievable for this market. That meant that for Toshiba, it was only sensible to keep all the work – design, manufacturing, selling – inside the house.

Even for earlier LSIs, logic chipsets built for custom functions, it only made sense to do everything on the platen of infrastructure that Toshiba had already put under its own roof.

But SOC splits the market. Customers come now in very small groupings, or one at a time. In the changing Silicon Valley market, the speed-to-completion and overhead-cutting models rely on *not* doing everything in one company, but quickly marshaling your competencies and parts with those offered by other specialists in the neighborhood.

Having Toshiba as a parent does have its value to ArTile: customers know the new start-up is implicitly backed by the world's second-largest chipmaker; Toshiba itself has many IPs of its own that can be drawn on; Toshiba has fabs world-famous for their quality and so can often get the manufacturing as well as the design jobs.

But still, there is a distinct difference in the business models of the giant and start-up. Insist on doing it all yourself – or insist on splitting the job quickly among those firms who can supply with the greatest competency at the greatest speed.

It's a challenge. What *isn't* in this business?

ArTile shuts itself off from the labs of its Toshiba colleagues, on the same floor of the same building, not just because it does business in a different way. Toshiba would ultimately like to go IPO (Initial Public Offering, the first sale on the securities market of stock shares in a heretofore private company) with ArTile. And indeed, all its engineers, highly specialized people who are not easy to find and must be kept satisfied with remuneration plans that are not the same as any other in Toshiba, are already guaranteed stock options for the day it does. But whether it will sell the whole company to the market, or maintain a controlling share, is a big difference that remains undecided. For the time being, ArTile and Toshiba want to underscore to clients, potential clients, and to the potential investment partners that may be among them, that this is a separate company, not just a working part of Toshiba.

The meaning of the distinction is as important to the owners as it is to the customers.

★

The chip business is mammoth, its products as differentiated as potato chips are from chocolate chips. But it is the nerve system of all of Toshiba Corp. not only for what its chip units sell, but for what part its chips play and will play in all of Toshiba's other product lines.

For that reason, it's important in understanding Toshiba's future to understand Toshiba's strategy for chips from here on. Radiating outward to the future from the core of the now-crushed DRAM business are four lines of change and development.

- The first line leads away from commodity DRAMs, which have been closed out as an unprofitable business through sale or shutting and conversion of its manufacturing facilities, and stretches through their descendants in the volatile memories line: chips like FCRAMs, which produce better margins, and on to non-volatile FeRAMs and flash memories like NAND, which have a chance to become volume leaders in the storage market someday.

- The second leads to discrete chips, which fulfill only one or a few fixed functions, but are ever-expanding in demand and are very profitable for Toshiba.

- The third takes Toshiba from the Emotion Engine – a chance opportunity – onward to System LSIs, and the kinds of advanced systems-on-a-chip that ArTile is building in California.

- And the fourth is the highly experimental world of Toshiba's own, in-house research & development, testing new circuitry and new materials and new manufacturing processes for open-horizon products like CELL, and many other silicon devices that will control Toshiba's own proprietary products and components, and find their ways from there to a ready world market of other producers.

"As you know, even Jesus wasn't welcomed by many in his own

place and time." The speaker is Tsuyoshi Kawanishi, the retired Toshiba senior executive vice-president who guided the seven semiconductor divisions of Toshiba in their heyday, the late 1980s. He spent forty years working in circuits for Toshiba, and that wasn't enough: after retirement he has served on the boards of several other semiconductor-related businesses, including Applied Materials of the US and two big manufacturers in Taiwan. And he has, perhaps prophetically, a message for Toshiba's chip-maker managers, derived from what he has seen since he was one of them.

"You know, the DRAM era is gone. This is the logic era, and in the logic era the important thing is time to market. So what I have learned is, when the customers ask 'when can you deliver?' the Taiwanese companies answer 'three days.' Toshiba's answer is more likely to be 'one month.' You see the point?"

That's not a specific case, just an example of the competition Toshiba is up against in the merchant business, for any chip. Japanese engineers including managers pursue always excellence and, closely related, cost-control in the product: in production yield, in machine capacity, whatever. That takes time. "But the Taiwanese look at it differently: they know if the chip price is ten dollars now, in a year it will be just one dollar. They have only a short time to take advantage of that high price.

"They take a higher yield loss in their factories to fill an order, because if the Taiwanese can get a yield of 70% from their lines but achieve the order 100% faster than a year, they capture the price advantage. And those who come in later are left with lower prices, and so even with a 100% yield of first-quality chips, they cannot make a profit.

"I don't know the real reason for this difference, but in our age, around the 1990s, everybody was thinking only of lowering cost – not the price. If we needed ten machines for a new line, the president would ask us to make do with nine. But in Taiwan if a manager requests ten machines, his executives will say, 'Oh, we'll give you eleven.' So that even if one machine stops working, the total line can still produce at 100%."

Of course what Kawanishi alludes to is Japan's philosophical approach to product and profit, the latter of which was never given much attention in any stage of Japan's industrial development. Japanese manufacturers of every type, while fully aware of the need to shorten the supply chain and delivery time to the customer, are famous for their first reliance on cutting cost within the production chain, to price more competitively and capture business in the market rather than to return profits, while maintaining always the same high quality.

But cost-cutting takes time. It is often done at the level of line workers themselves, spotting chokepoints or production problems once the manufacturing has already begun.

One can't help but wonder: is the age of that paradigm now dying? And if it is, how will Toshiba's managers get around the paradox as the future closes in? Tough questions for the Semiconductor Company, and for Toshiba Corp. itself, and both have realized it.

Beginning in late 2001, Toshiba Semiconductor Company switched to a new plan for basic supply-chain management, which it calls the Global One System. Customer queries and requests now go to a centralized command system, which will give a response, including date of delivery, within 24 hours. This alone used to take up to five days. The Global One System also places orders for materials to produce the requested semiconductors, and Toshiba's plants will now go into operation producing new orders within ten days of their receipt.

In future, Toshiba aims to cut that order-to-production lead time to just 24 hours, by applying ever more sophisticated information technology to refine the Global One System.

But whether Global One is the final answer or not, the

greatest likelihood is that Toshiba's solution will center not on the abandonment of either cost-controls or quality, but on the better use of technology to achieve more of both.

NOTES

1. "Toshiba: A Giant Struggles To Reinvent Itself," *Business Week* Asian Edition, New York, 13 October 1997
2. "Semiconductor firms raise industry investment," *Yomiuri Shimbun*, Tokyo, 7 October 2000
3. Quoted in Martin Fransman, *Japan's Computer and Communications Industry: The Evolution of Industrial Giants and Global Competitiveness*, Oxford University Press, Oxford and New York, 1995
4. Ibid.

CHAPTER TWELVE
A DISPLAY OF PERSEVERANCE

Toru Shima was a man with a problem: people. More than that, these were special kinds of people – engineers, a whole team of them, who all had to agree on what needed doing and when, before anything they were assigned to could get done.

And they were in disagreement.

Shima was picked by Toshiba in 1989 to run a new and exotic – and very important – joint venture between his company and the most sophisticated computer manufacturer in the world, IBM. But it wasn't to build computers.

No, Display Technologies Inc. (DTI) was tasked with creating something new altogether: full-color liquid crystal display devices, which it would take from just a concept all the way through to a product rolling off a manufacturing line.

But Shima was a semiconductor man, not a display specialist. And all these Toshiba and IBM engineers around him couldn't really be specialists either, because no one knew how to make a product that didn't yet exist.

But they were already arguing over it.

Shima had successfully presided over a microchip joint venture between Toshiba and Motorola of the US in the late 1980s, but this was different: this venture conjoined roughly equal numbers of Japanese engineers from each of the competitive sides. Men who were long accustomed to the R&D methodologies of their own employers, and saw no reason why the other side couldn't adopt them. As a result, no one was adopting anything. And time was already beginning to run out for Shima and his infant venture in the plant in Himeji, near Osaka.

He thought it over, and came to a conclusion. "My biggest job was to make them forget they came from separate companies, make them understand they were now working for a brand-new company, DTI. Each of them just had different conceptions of how the schedule should run, and they couldn't coordinate with each other. So I made them forget about their conceptions."

How? "I did anything and everything I could. Sometimes I went to meetings the IBM team had with their own bosses, just to be there. Sometimes I went out drinking with the project teams."

To drive the collegial concept home, Shima admits, he actually placed a large jar on the table in DTI's meeting room, and enforced a penalty of ten yen to be pitched into the jar each time a participant mentioned the name of his own home company.

Eventually the suasion worked, the engineers began looking hard at each other's ideas – and the product was created and the lines were rolling by October 1991.

The story of DTI is more than just a cautionary of the kinds of difficulties ventures staffed by strong-minded specialists can encounter. It says a great deal about corporate alliance strategy in the digital industry – and shows how far back and on what a large scale it has operated.

Both companies decided internally they would be forced by competition to come up with color LCDs in the 1990s. But as neither side had all the expertise necessary – Toshiba was an expert at semiconductor production, the same type of technology LCDs require; IBM was very good at the logic designs that would control the displays – and as the investment required would be huge, they both looked outside for a partnership.

Of course the two are otherwise major competitors. But both

knew the product cycle for this invention would be just as shaky as the product cycle for PCs and for chips themselves, and that other technologies now unknown might well emerge as contenders if they didn't act with the greatest speed possible.

In the end they decided on a fifty-fifty development and manufacturing investment, with all products to be used for their own PCs – and perhaps later, if production could be ramped up, for resale as merchant components to other manufacturers.

The two partners sank a collective 250 million dollars into DTI, and Shima was left to sort out the personnel conflicts, plus the mess of ordering machines and costly materials for people who weren't sure how to use them, from people who weren't sure how to prepare them.

By 1993, DTI produced 304,000 displays and IBM was ready to double the company's production by opening a new line at its own Japan plant, in Yasu.

Probably nothing except window glass and the earth's atmosphere gets looked through more and seen less by humans than liquid crystal displays. They're on your calculator, your digital wristwatch, your programmable coffee-maker, your dashboard, your digital alarm clock, your thermostat, your cellular phone, small TVs, portable computer screens – and on and on.

They may be ubiquitous. But it hasn't been easy to put them there. The technology is complex, equal in some stages to creating a semiconductor chip itself.

Their basic construction is simple enough: two thin sheets of glass, sandwiching a vacuum perhaps one-fifth as wide as a human hair, into which the conductive liquid crystal material is injected. The hard part is engraving a microscopic grid on the outside of the top glass sheet, and then embedding thousands and thousands of electrodes (or electrical conductors), each with a tiny wire connecting it to a central logic chip. The logic chip directs the current to the proper when-and-where, and the diodes waiting at each intersection of the grid create the image, and changes in it, as the current is redirected. All that engraving is done in the same basic way a microchip is engraved. But no microchip has a flat surface measuring 14 inches diagonally. The larger the working surface, the greater the probability that the slightest defect or mishap in the smallest corner of the glass will ruin the whole display — and thus the more sophisticated the technology needed to stabilize and perfect its creation.

To add color to the equation, tiny dots of red, green, and blue phosphor had to be imprinted on the back side of the surface sheet, and the timing of the charges sent to the diode altered to take account not only of light and dark, but of all the combinations of those three bits, repeated everywhere on the screen, that turn the image into glorious full color.

Tough. But they did it.

Four floors high, with four clean rooms on each to assure no impurities touched the glass surfaces in manufacture, the DTI Himeji plant sped its production lines up faster and faster, and DTI's parents, Toshiba and IBM, began supplying color imagery displays not only to their own factories but to huge quadrants of the world of its competitors. Things were humming all through the 1990s. They came to a stop only once: on the morning of 17 January 1995.

That is when the Great Hanshin Earthquake struck, just 40 kilometers away. In a matter of hours 6,400 were dead across the region, elevated highways were toppled along with high-rise buildings, trains were hurled from their tracks and huge fires broke out. Property losses eventually registered $120 billion.

Shima leapt out his front door within minutes of the tremor and raced to the plant, where outside the damage appeared slight but inside it was heart-sinkingly heavy. At least, however, no one working the morning shift had been killed or seriously injured. Instead the building just stood there, eerily quiet . . .

★   ★   ★

Six years after the earth shook Shima's world, the company president of Toshiba Display Devices and Components Co. can still set even tougher targets for his manufacturing and worldwide sales. "The goal of Toshiba's Display Devices & Components Systems is, basically, to get one of the top – *the* top, if possible – market positions in the LCD business, using the most advanced position in the world in silicon technology," explains Eisaburo Hamano.

Simple enough to say.

But the means themselves are a bit more complex. While the DTI lines were moving along smartly in Himeji and Yasu, Toshiba had already gone back to the engineering computers to learn how to adapt a more sophisticated material, polysilicon, to the LCD technology.

The difference in using polysilicon is that it permits the charging technology to more finely adapt and control the current leading-edge technology of imaging by thin-film transistors rather than by diodes. A close meshwork of almost invisibly tiny transistors overlays the top of the screen now. With this permitting so many more, so much smaller elements to be crowded onto the surface, polysilicon's much faster speed of change in charging – from about 30 to 100 times faster than the switching speed of the old LCD color technology – takes advantage of the transistors' own much faster response times and gives a much more fluid motion to moving images, plus a much greater image definition.

Toshiba feels this is the color display technology of the foreseeable future, and having perfected both the design and manufacturing technology itself, is ready to plunge vast sums to establish it as such.

Of course with Toshiba, the world's largest maker of portable computers with whole volumes of plans to move heavily into Personal Digital Assistants and 3G display-equipped cell phones in the next year, as the first customer in line for its own displays, the company is already in a promising position, marketing-wise, to make that wish start coming true. Toshiba was already producing polysilicon LCDs in a small factory, and so all the kinks had been worked out of the system when Hamano spoke.

Hamano was, in mid 2001, facing a difficult demand situation, due to stagnant economies in Japan and the US, and a big slowdown in Europe, both inside Toshiba and in the merchant market which he hoped to claim. And other firms were experimenting with the same materials, though they had produced little to date.

But he knew the cards were with him.

★   ★   ★

On the fourth floor of the stricken DTI plant that morning in 1995, Shima saw the worst: the ceiling had collapsed, destroying all four of the clean rooms there. Time to act.

The quake had hit just after 5 a.m. Ambulances squealed in the background; horrible images were flowing across the television screens.

By 7:30 a.m. all of his managers had checked on their people to make sure everyone was OK, and were formed in a somber circle around him on the first floor. Shima knew his boss, the Toshiba Display Division Chief, was on business out of the country. He also knew that a shutdown of his plant here would seriously disrupt manufacturing of computers and other products in his customers' plants all around the world.

He dispatched some volunteers to drive over the accordioned roads toward the epicenter, near metropolitan Kobe, and check out transportation clearances around the area. He sent others out to see how his component and material suppliers had fared.

And when the workers were assembled, of course he permitted those who wished to go into Kobe and volunteer their rescue services there – several of the employees had relatives living in the area. Then he turned around and paid attention to cleaning up the damage at DTI. He wondered how many weeks he could squeeze recovery into.

The cracks and splits in the building itself would take a year to repair.

But the plant inside restarted operation, on all floors but the fourth, the very next day.

No IBM people, no Toshiba people were clearing, repairing, adjusting and running the delicate machines: only DTI people were.

President Hamano has a fairly good reason to think he's holding the winning cards.

Because this time he launches full-scale production of polysilicon LCDs in another joint venture, a factory in Singapore. He owns 67% of what will eventually be the 750-employee AFPD Pte., Ltd., opening in mid 2002 in Singapore. Matsushita Electric Industrial owns and is financing the other 33%.

Of course, just to be on the safe side, Toshiba will keep other LCD lines rolling at Fukaya. In fact, to be safer still, Toshiba announced in October 2001 that it and Matsushita had decided to go ahead and merge all of their LCD and next-generation display business into a single joint venture, to be 60% owned by Toshiba, by April 2002.

It is ironic that at about the same time the Singapore plant announcement was issued, IBM revealed it was deciding, by terms of its venture contract, to end its own DTI involvement, which produced in its eleven-year run 21.3 million LCDs. Toshiba will keep Himeji; IBM will keep Yasu; both will keep the production coming out.

But IBM has also tied up in a venture with Chi Mei Optoelectronics in Taiwan,[1] a move unsurprising in the face of the logic of the global market structure, which has brought new Korean and Taiwanese competitors into the 16-billion-dollar arena and cut prices down by 50%.[2]

In fact, almost all Japanese computer-display LCD makers have by now formed partnerships of one sort or another, either ventures or OEM supply contracts, to cut costs and risks.

But obscure as the future may seem in the display industry, Toshiba will give up neither the product nor the strategy. Early in 2001, Japan's newspapers carried a brief story revealing that *all* of Japan's six big electronics makers were already forming a fifty-million-yen joint venture for development of the *next* generation of liquid crystal displays.[3] Of course one name among the six is Toshiba Corp., and of course it will dispatch more engineers to join the joint research team.

NOTES

1. "LCD makers pair up to shoulder risk," *Nikkei Weekly*, Tokyo, August 2001
2. "IBM, Toshiba calling halt to LCD output," *Nikkei Weekly*, Tokyo, 21 May 2001
3. "Six electronics makers tie up on research for new LCDs," *The Japan Times*, Tokyo, 6 February 2001

CHAPTER THIRTEEN
THE LESSONS OF COCOM

You can still see the spare, 82-year-old silhouette of Shoichi Saba in the hallways of the executive floor of Toshiba's headquarters, which he yet visits daily as a Senior Advisor to the corporation.

The impossibility of the COCOM crisis may have forced him out of the chairman's job at the time his husbandry of the company was about to flower into its most profitable products and technologies. But apparently, to his successors it never tarnished the wisdom of his counsel.

"The concept of Toshiba as a group was very different then," is the way Chairman Taizo Nishimuro explains the crisis. "President Doko had tried very hard [in the 1970s] to strengthen the Toshiba group, and in doing that he encouraged the subsidiaries to take their own independent positions – to do whatever they felt needed doing, without consulting the parent company. The subsidiaries were to be equal to and independent of the parent company.

"But that was not followed up by a common code of conduct, or by a reporting system that whatever seemed necessary but might be illegal had first to be reported to the parent. There were no safety measures. And what they [the Toshiba Machine subsidiary] did was indeed an intentional violation. It was really an embarrassment."

Equally – or perhaps more – embarrassed was Tetsuo Kadoya, a young staffer who, with family, had been sent to work in the

Dallas office just before all of this boiled over. Kadoya (today the senior vice-president of Toshiba America and the Government and Industry Relations General Manager stationed in Washington, DC) had some personal distractions of his own. First son Kentaro was just at the age to enter first grade, and though he spoke no English that grade was going to be a Texan one.

"My wife and I had a lot of trepidations. But the principal took him straight to the first-grade classroom and introduced him to the teacher, and she in turn introduced him personally to every student in the room." As Kentaro stood, stoically and formally shaking the hand of every one of them, the Kadoyas breathed a low, sweet sigh of relief. This was going to be OK.

"A few days later we dropped by the school again, as classes were let out, to make sure things were all right. We couldn't see Kentaro; he was kept behind. We had all kinds of frightening visions of some trouble he had gotten into." But when they peeked from the corridor through the window of the classroom door, what they saw was their son's teacher spending her own after-class time helping Kentaro learn his English. "We were very impressed."

The anxious family from Tokyo soon was put at ease, and it wasn't long before Kadoya, doing the Saturday shopping in a nearby supermarket, heard a "howdy," felt a slap on his back, and received a welcome to the neighborhood and, in fact, an invitation to a backyard barbecue party that very night.

"A little while later our office was moved to a nearby industrial park, and we had planned a party but then canceled it. So I took the money set aside, and gave televisions and videocassette recorders to all the schools in the district."

At the annual school board budget meeting, Kadoya was bewildered to be singled out and asked to the podium, where he received a standing ovation. "The mayor of Dallas and the district school superintendent were right there!" And that was good.

★

Because three months later the COCOM incident erupted.

"Tokyo told us to hold our tongues, to do nothing. But my 80 American employees urged us to speak up, and in fact they themselves began a letter-writing campaign from friends and family, producing more than 100 grass-roots support pleas to Congress.

"I decided I could not do nothing. I took a few of the letters, and called and asked for an appointment with the local office of the Congressman representing our district. He happened to be in town himself, and he agreed to see me, I think because we were an employer in good standing in his constituency."

In the lawmaker's office Kadoya introduced and explained himself, took a seat, and reached into the folder of letters to open one at random.

"It was from a Mexican-American working in our warehouse. He explained openly that he had entered the US illegally, then gotten his status straightened out and come to work for us. Our foreman had sponsored him for a working residence and then for a green card [permanent residence status], and he wrote all this and about how much he loved the US and how faithful Toshiba had been to him."

The Congressman listened to the end. "I felt all alone in presenting something that seemed so emotional, and when I was done reading the Congressman had to ask me, 'Mister Kadoya, is that a tear in your eye?'

"I told him how much my business, mainly supplying US military Post-Exchange stores, had been hurt – gone almost to nothing – and how unfair this was to all our American employees. He said he was impressed, and asked if he could come and visit our operation.

"We had only a small showroom, but on the day he came, the 350 people crowded shoulder-to-shoulder inside it made it look even smaller. In the front, there were just two visitors

dressed in suits for the occasion: the district school superintendent, and the mayor of Dallas. The superintendent actually said
something to the Representative like 'Sir, you are our Congressman. But if you do anything in Washington to hurt this company,
you don't represent us.' "

With that kind of influence (and at least 350 votes on the line),
what kind of Congressman isn't going to come away from that
visit very impressed?

It wasn't too much longer before the resignations in Tokyo,
and things blew over quickly in that district of Dallas for Toshiba.

The story makes a heart-warming bromide – but it's more than
that. In aggregate both the COCOM violation and aftermath,
and the kind of experience Toshiba's men on the line overseas,
like Kadoya, were having taught the company its first big lesson
in globalization – in those seminal days, still thought of as only a
gestural "internationalization," a kind of ritual to genuflect
before those societies who were Toshiba's best customers
overseas.

COCOM, the agreement to restrict furnishing of certain
security-sensitive supplies and technologies to Soviet-bloc or
other communist states, was a vestige of the Cold War era at the
time of Toshiba's troubles. But it was compounded as a bilateral
political explosion by two other factors: a growing frustration
over seemingly insoluble trade arguments between Japan and
the US themselves, and also the growing possibilities to find
customers, and serve them, on the other side of the COCOM
wall if a violator were willing, made possible by the rapidly
expanding economic and trading networks that before too long
would be termed Globalism.

Globalism, the opening of doors, windows, and chutes to
trade and investment across almost every political boundary, was
real, and it had begun calling for great care and responsibility on

the part of every company with international interests, when considered in the context of national security and international security alliances.

The COCOM incident rudely demonstrated to Japan that its old policy, of separating politics from economics as if the two had nothing to do with each other, no longer applied. The anger, justified or not, that Americans felt over growing trade imbalances with Japan also played a rough part in focusing so much attention on the violation of COCOM by the Toshiba subsidiary.

International relations were something more than a matter of trade relations. In fact they were becoming a matter of deep concern for corporate governance. Saba, after he had resigned and become a Toshiba advisor years later, had the idea of creating a panel of international advisors, which gathered twice a year with Toshiba executives to discuss "international affairs." But the panelists − all heads of world-recognized corporations and organizations themselves − were told politely that they should never make so bold as to comment on affairs of current business of the Corporation. "This was very strange," thought Taizo Nishimuro as he took over presidency of Toshiba. He changed it.

Toshiba rethought its real position in the profitable sun of world economic integration and the international advisors, who still meet twice a year, are now encouraged to bring up any subject they like. "One problem is their unwillingness to take advice," growls one senior European executive who sits on the panel. But at least, now they hear it.

"When I became the CEO, I made it a point to give clear instructions to all members of the Toshiba family that the Doko principle is not right, and is dead," recalls Nishimuro. "And this year we have completed our new Toshiba Code of Conduct. I have made sure that it takes effect among all subsidiaries as well as within the parent company."

Under Chapter 3 of the 26-page Toshiba Standards of Conduct, Paragraph 1 Section (3) says it all: ". . . Toshiba shall not enter into any transaction involving products subject to export restrictions and failing to comply with the export control laws and regulations in each of the countries and areas where Toshiba operates, and those of the United States where applicable."

Nishimuro has done more than issue the right commands. He has expanded the department of statutory auditors, established as a requirement under Japanese commercial code for all corporations, and charged them with certifying that all terms of all contracts, all agreements of Toshiba subsidiaries and parent company alike, are vetted thoroughly.

The Standards of Conduct is only a document. Auditing Toshiba's actual dealings is a minefield. Just ask Tomoyasu Uchiyama, Chief Specialist of the Corporate Audit Division. He's one of the men who has to do that certifying.

A recurring headache of the Audit Division is problems in distribution, Uchiyama says. Toshiba sells its products into many channels – full of dealers who sometimes resell them to who knows where? "In Africa, in the Middle East, in Southeast Asia, there are a great mix of rules and regulations from border to border. There are many markets – and there are smugglers.

"A simple example of what we have to be careful of would be a direct sale from us to a Japanese trading company. Terms of the sale would include commitment to obey all international laws and agreements. But that company might bring the product out of Japan and sell it in a country with, say, no agreement to observe COCOM restrictions. Things can be mishandled at *that* level without our knowing anything about it.

"Maybe they even say Toshiba suggested this, which of course we did not. But the product turns up in the wrong place, and people look at the label on it, and draw utterly wrong conclusions about how it got there. In such cases we would be questioned of course, so we have to keep careful records of all the restrictions we write on the contract, showing that the sale was indeed conditional on observance of COCOM plus local law, etc.

"This doesn't happen a lot. But still it happens often enough that we must watch constantly, and oftentimes we ask [independent] traders who buy from us to provide letters of guarantee they will honor national customs and tax laws and so on. Whether they actually do or don't, we can do nothing about."

Uchiyama sometimes travels to places as far as Mexico and Southeast Asia to review the contracts of the Toshiba subsidiaries on the spot: "procurement deals, real-estate, construction, sales agreements, warranties, all manner of things." His department of 80 is staffed nowadays with few accountants, but many specialists such as lawyers, managers, sales personnel, production specialists: those who know what to look for in each corner and crevice of the fine print.

Still, Uchiyama himself does not think Toshiba takes a strong enough stand in defending itself. "Toshiba is a very pure kind of company, always measuring profit versus risk. In most of our contentions the problems are not criminal but civil: questions of financial responsibility. Some countries take these matters to court, which Toshiba's staff thinks of as a very special matter. So, to avoid court they settle. And they don't explain their positions, which may well be the right ones. They just escape the matter.

"People today, as I say, always talk about global standards. But actually there is no single global standard in the world: there is a mix-up of many of them. So Toshiba in future has to have the power and the technique to read all those differences. To protect itself. For Toshiba people to just keep on this way, it's very pure but not tough. And actually, we have to recognize that business is indeed very tough."

CHAPTER FOURTEEN
WORKING TOGETHER

Interviewer: What is your enterprise vision for Toshiba?

Chairman Nishimuro: We should remain [only] in those businesses where we can be one of the top three players in the world. I don't mean that Toshiba can independently be one of the top three – our strategies include combinations or alliances with other parties, through which together we can achieve and remain at the rank of one of the world's top three.

You have to see it the chairman's way, see alliances not just as one more strategy in the corporate toolbox, but as a key philosophy which can convert an enterprise's problems into potentials for victory, to understand why Toshiba is so aggressive at forming corporate alliances for so many purposes.

It might be an arrangement with Electrolux, to stay atop the domestic home-appliance market. It might be an LSI basic-research partnership with Sony, to capture the video-game-console market. It might be a tie-up with Matsushita, to produce common components in quantity, like LCDs, for the merchant market as well as for Toshiba products themselves.

All of them tributaries, rolling down the stream of products and technologies to form the river of Toshiba, which at last reaches the sea of the world's markets as one of the three biggest rivers of enterprise in those sectors of the electronic/electrical continent.

★

It's a strategy that colors the corporate culture, as we've seen in other chapters, and one long familiar to the Toshiba managerial infrastructure. Back in the early 1900s, Toshiba contracted to supply General Electric with light-bulb filaments. It both learned and profited: eventually GE invested half of Toshiba's prewar capital (and even, for a time, sent an American to serve as its president).

The strategy resumed with many more alliances after the war and in 1993, with a list of major allies that then included Apple Computer, Asahi Chemical, Ericsson, GEC Alsthom, GE, LSI Logic of Canada, Motorola, National Semiconductor, Olivetti, Rhone-Poulenc, Samsung, SGS Thomson, Siemens, Sun Microsystems, Telic Alcatel, Thomson Consumer Electronics, Time Warner, and United Technologies, Toshiba's then-president Fumio Sato put into words what had become obvious: "The technology has become so advanced, and the markets so complex, that you simply can't expect to be the best at the whole process any longer."[1]

You also can't, no matter how big your company, afford to keep the many R&D projects in the air that Toshiba must at all times, with your own checkbook. Any one or two big failures, whether in the lab or in the marketplace, could by themselves sink the whole company.

Sharing risk from the R&D phase onward cuts the chances of such apocalyptic outcomes – and in fact is an added guarantee of success at the market end of the joint project, because each participant will itself be purchasing, using, or reselling the finished product.

And since the kind of alliance partners Toshiba chooses are themselves among the world-class players in their industries, the odds of the partners together reaching that rank of the top three in the field are that much better, once the product is launched.

Toshiba's Major Global Strategic Alliances (as of 2001)★

Infineon (FeRAM)
Electrolux (home appliances)
Microsoft ("ebook")
SanDisk (Flash memory, memory cards)
United Technologies (fuel cells)
Sony (.07-micron process technology)
IBM, Sony Computer Entertainment (next-generation processor)
Canon (next-generation flat-display, silicon wafers)
General Electric (power generation, turbine rotors, drive systems)
Time Warner (multimedia content)
Carrier (air conditioners)
Matsushita (LCDs, CRT procurement, memory cards)
Fujitsu (DRAM process technology)
Hitachi/Matsushita (digital-TV-commerce platform)

★Toshiba has many other alliances with smaller organizations as well, both domestic and international.

At times the alliance strategy has been brilliantly successful: Toshiba played a catch-up game in semiconductors through the 1980s, but in 1987 a 1.2-billion-dollar joint venture with Motorola allowed it to supply its American partner with OEM DRAM memories and to gain access to then cutting-edge know-how in microprocessor design and manufacturing. It was in these years that Toshiba hit No. 2 chipmaker in the world.

At other times, success has arrived on a more oblique traject-ory. Toshiba's investment of a billion dollars in Time Warner's entertainment properties didn't seem to be going much of anywhere, until the idea of movies for home viewing on 12-centimeter optical disks popped up, in the mid 1990s. The DVD story, which is told in the next chapter, shows most clearly how these alliances, far from coming along in propitious strokes of good fortune, follow from clear-eyed, carefully crafted, shrewdly targeted – and often enough hard-fought – maneuvering aimed at each partner's best interests.

As this was written, in the fall of 2001, Toshiba and Matsushita announced a decision for strategic merger of the LCD businesses, existing and next-generation, not just to produce components for each but to "work for early standardization of design methodologies and manufacturing processes." The future will include promoting quick commercialization of organic light-emitting diode displays, which are considered to be the coming generation of flat-screen television displays.

Toshiba and Matsushita, before this Nos. 5 and 6 respectively in the LCD fields at home, now rank second in Japan's industry, as an alliance.[2]

As if that weren't enough, the same two firms on the very same day announced yet another joint venture, to enjoy the economies of joint procurement of parts and materials for manufacture of the color cathode ray tubes (TV and monitor tubes) and video-projection tubes of each. Not to *manufacture* them together, as with flat-screen displays: just to "work on standardization of components, cost-reduction scheme(s), and development of global supplier sources."

Just going shopping together, to negotiate in numbers and get price breaks on bulk buying, is reason enough for a strategic alliance today.

The new generation of System Integration businesses is also the newest promise for Toshiba's alliance strategy. Aiming to provide small businesses with scaled-down versions of the information-technology networks that the big boys use, Toshiba has just formed a joint venture with Oracle, who can provide economical packaged software, and consultants Accenture, who supply advice on how to use it best, that will install small Toshiba computers, servers, and communications technology, all in one simple solutions-oriented package.

And from what it is learning in this small-scale type of systems integration, Toshiba is forming another style of alliance: that of its own, in-house companies, to make product networks that are more than the sum of their parts.

Imagine household integration of digital, interactive TVs with built-in hard-disk-drive memories, of wireless phones and wireless portable computers, of GPS satellite location-finders, voice-recognition controls, always-on Internet access, and household machines such as water-sprinkler timers, heaters and coolers, electric blankets and kitchen appliances.

Imagine all these working through the control of a single home server – and remember that most of these things, very nearly all of them, are made and installed by Toshiba's in-house companies themselves – and you have pictured yet another business alliance that is already beginning to take shape within the corporation itself.

Many competitors can see this kind of synthesis arriving, too. Will Toshiba wind up as one of the top three? The question it might ask in response is, who else makes all of these things under a single corporate roof? And if the competitors don't have all the parts to make such a system integration – who is likely to be waiting for them when they turn around and look for a source of supply?

NOTES

1. "Toshiba Makes Global Alliances Work," *Fortune Magazine*, New York, 4 October 1993
2. "Toshiba, Matsushita bid for supremacy in LCDs," *Asahi Shimbun*, Tokyo, 20 October 2001

CHAPTER FIFTEEN
DVD: AD ASTRA PER ASPERA

Sometimes, when a corporation follows a dream, it has to have a few lucky stars line up to make it come true. And sometimes they only line up with a bit of a push.

One of the greatest of Toshiba's corporate alliance stories gave birth to the technology and the market success of Digital Versatile Disk: DVD. Roughly a million disk drives, both for viewing home video and for installation as computer memory media, were expected to be sold in 2001 alone, and disks bearing the software are circulating in the billions.

How DVD got invented, and got adopted by the world, is a tale with a plot line so twisted Hollywood would never think of trying to equal it on-screen.

It begins with a man named Hisashi Yamada, watching the fascinating struggle of formats that gave birth to Pioneer's Laser-Disc pre-recorded movie players in the early 1980s, from his laboratory at Toshiba's Corporate Research & Development Center, and thinking that he and his colleagues could surely do better.

And it continues with a man named Koji Hase, brooding at the rainswept city through the window of Toshiba's corporate headquarters tower, where he had just relocated, in 1984, from an assignment selling consumer electronics in London. Wondering what to do with himself.

Yamada could see plainly that the Pioneer format left much to be desired: it was an analog picture, not a digital one. At 12 inches across, like an old LP, it was too big, and like an LP it had to be manually flipped halfway through the movie.

By 1982 Philips and Sony had debuted their new pre-recorded musical disk and player, the CD (Compact Disc). It was to become world-sweepingly popular, with its digital-quality music reproduction – and Yamada began to envision a disk of about the same size for movies. But this wouldn't be easy, he knew: the problems lay less in storing so much digital information on such a small surface, than on the signal-processing technology – which would have to be controlled by a large-scale integrated circuits microchip built into the player.

Oh, that too was a solvable problem, of course. But only at the kind of expense that would have made any player prohibitively costly to consumers. Yamada began to think in terms of the life-cycles of technology of the television: it took 20 years to take black and white TV to color TV. It took another 20 years to create and popularize the videocassette recorder-player.

On top of those known facts, there were others: DRAM memories had been quadrupling their capacity every three years, and the technology to make them had of course allowed similar progress in etching control circuits on microprocessors. "So if you want to achieve increased sophistication in signal processing through LSI, then by waiting three years you can produce it at a quarter of the cost of today." Simple arithmetic gave a likely time when the disk-controller LSI would be achieved at a price the consumer could afford to pay. Yamada figured out that, yes, all the factors would come together on a store shelf in about 20 years.

It's good to have a plan.

And now he had one, so he set to work. That work was delayed while he took a three-year hiatus in the semiconductor laboratories to upgrade his own skills in logic LSIs and project-team management, but no research on a good idea at Toshiba ever gets truly sidetracked.

It just gets laid aside until the proper time.

Twenty years was not the kind of range that Koji Hase wanted to plan for in seeking his next market success. The end of this month would be good.

But that, he guessed, wouldn't be in the cards either, because "my mission was to find a new type of consumer product that would go beyond" the regular audiovisual goods he had taken to market in the UK. And the new-product-type cookie jar at Toshiba wasn't yielding anything that pleased anyone much.

First out of the gate was a digital still camera, which sold – or rather, didn't sell – for about five thousand dollars. Sony already had a product in the field, and cut its price soon to half of Hase's: no easy solution there.

Then there was digital audiotape, a medium that seemed promising back around the middle 1980s. But it never promised the music-recording industry enough. They told manufacturers they were quite satisfied with CD music disks and regular tape cassettes, thanks, and didn't need any other formats. So that was the end of that idea.

Philips, meanwhile, had taken the CD concept further to CD-ROM in 1985. Hase noticed this, and got an idea for using its navigation capabilities – quick access to information stored anywhere on the CD – to build a new product. "I used to call the early versions of my idea 'electronic secretary,' holding all the addresses, phone and fax numbers, and so on.

"So I developed a big CD-ROM drive, with big capacity, which nobody wanted to buy because nobody could use 800 megabytes of memory. So," he sighs, "from '86 to '87, '88, virtually nothing happened." Then one day, something did.

"Hewlett-Packard suddenly sent us a huge order, several thousand drives a month. They had discovered a use for them: installing software quickly in computers." H-P had seen that the dozen or more floppy disks used to load software packages, which took hours to pump their new programs into the computers, could be replaced by a single CD-ROM. The rest began to look like history: by the end of the 1980s, Toshiba was shipping 20,000 drives a month for building into computers, and by the time DVD rolled around half a decade later, that figure was up to 800,000 units per month.

"Because of the uniqueness and novelty of the features, we earned a very good profit margin of 10 to 15% each. That was very good indeed. And I was rich."

Well, Toshiba was rich. Or getting richer, anyway – enough to take the first step toward the alliance that would produce DVD. Early in the 1990s, Hase was named to a Toshiba negotiating team that eventually bought part of Time Warner Inc., with the idea of having a stake in the content business. The talks took a long while and Hase exchanged business cards with dozens of TW executives – including one who would turn out to be a very special acquaintance, Warren Lieberfarb, the president of Warner Home Video.

Lieberfarb, says Hase, was a man driven. "He was scared to death over the future of the television broadcast – that digital satellite broadcasting might kill his VHS tapes business. Warner Home Video had experimented successfully with direct sale, not just rental, of pre-recorded videotapes, and Lieberfarb was looking for a next-generation medium – especially one with an encryption code to block illegal copying – to carry movie sales into . . . well, the next generation." Some accounts have him claiming he was the first person to see that digitalized video would take the shape of a 12-cm disk, the same circumference as a CD – but he hadn't met Hisashi Yamada then.

Hase was the conduit between these two dreams. He called

Lieberfarb in his Burbank, California office and asked for a meeting. Lieberfarb said he could spare 30 minutes.

"When I met Warren I explained what I could offer: digital-picture, large-capacity, small CD-sized optical disk. He said the American movie viewer wants a high-quality picture, high-quality sound. A two-hour movie on one single disk. And there were all these reports saying that digital broadcasting was nearly there: people were talking about video on demand, anytime, using the phone lines and fiber cables." So, with digital television on demand threatening his very business, Lieberfarb had reason to worry.

He had, in fact, turned earlier to Philips for an answer, Hase recalls, and "was unhappy with their proposal – he was in search of somebody who could offer anything else. He spoke about it for hours, bending our discussion beyond a half an hour to six p.m., quitting time.

"And then he picked up the phone and called Morton's steak house, which is usually packed with Hollywood stars and moguls. And there was a table free. So we went there, started to drink, and by about 11:30 that night we realized we had a deal. I mean, I could promise anything after four bottles of Mondavi red."

Lieberfarb was a recognized and influential business power in Hollywood, Hase was aware, and a man who kept his word.

"So I went back to Tokyo and started to talk about this. Everybody laughed at first, because what Warren wanted required from 3 to 4 gigabytes of information on a single disk. CD at that time gave a maximum of 800 megabytes. So the density required simply meant compression technology had to be used." And there, Mister Hase met Mister Yamada.

Twelve years had passed since Mister Yamada's intuition. And LSI technology had advanced and its price had dropped, of course, by a factor of 16 times. Yamada was preparing to fight his own battle to set the standard for the new digital versatile disk – when along came Hase, Lieberfarb, and that agreement.

Now things, all done in the name of alliance, get complicated. To save time Yamada took the concept to Matsushita Electric Industrial, which had a trove of optical technology of its own. Together they came up with a 12-cm plastic disk just 0.6 millimeters thick. With two layers glued together, there was more than enough space for a full-length feature movie.

This took a while. Yamada had never met Lieberfarb and in February 1993, ten months later, he received an invitation to the proverbial 30 minutes in the latter's California office, to show what he had accomplished. "I told him my story. And he was really excited. He canceled all his other appointments, and our discussion ran through to the dinner hour. So he took me to Morton's steak house. The only thing he didn't like was that the drive unit was not compatible with music CDs. That, he wanted."

The next step was to reconcile the effort with Philips, which was then considered part of a three-way alliance to take the development the next few steps along. Things were cordial at first; but then Yamada was shown in mid 1993 a different prototype that Philips had originated on its own.

Yamada hastened back to Tokyo and finished his prototype by late in the year. But four months later, Philips dissolved the Time Warner and Toshiba alliance, and eventually rejoined its own partnership with Sony, where collaboration on the audio CD had proven so successful.

Worse, reported *Business Week* Magazine at the time,[1] Matsushita was considering backing away from Toshiba and signing on with the new Philips and Sony collaboration team. There was evidence the three were planning to announce their own world standard soon. Lieberfarb at this time took another hand that showed a new truth to hardware makers all over the world:

it was the content owners who would, in this age, decide what products their movies would be shown on.

Lieberfarb, says *Business Week,* assembled an ad hoc committee in Hollywood composed of top people from each of seven big studios, with Walt Disney Co. and MGM/UA Home Entertainment chairing it. The Philips–Sony team apparently thought that Sony's control of the former Columbia Pictures would help swing the weight of Hollywood industry opinion behind its format.

But in late summer, "the ad hoc studio committee released a wish list that played straight into Toshiba's hands. They wanted 135 minutes of playing time, high image and audio quality, and room for at least three languages, plus a parental 'lockout' feature to skip over violent and risqué scenes . . . Toshiba's ten-gigabyte prototype had room to spare."[2]

Philips and Sony did not surrender, but Matsushita, for reasons of its own, eventually went back to the Toshiba format and the horizons were beginning to clear for the Hase and Yamada team. Finally on 24 January 1995, Toshiba, Hitachi, Matsushita, Pioneer, Thomson (makers of RCA), Time Warner, MGM, MCA, and Turner Home Video turned out in Hollywood to announce to the press their backing of the Toshiba format.

Space does not permit recounting all the details and intrigues of this major battle for the next world standard in optical disks. At least one former Toshiba PR officer relished his account of a tactic with the foreign press: it seems, having caught wind of the intention of Philips and Sony to announce their technology as a "world standard" in December 1994, Tetsuo Kadoya took the initiative of calling correspondents in Tokyo from the *Wall Street Journal,* the *Financial Times,* and the *New York Times* to make sure they got the "full story." Kadoya got busy on the telephone to the US, making arrangements with the ad hoc committee Lieberfarb had pulled together. When the correspondents expressed doubt to Kadoya that such big studios were lining up with Toshiba and not with Philips/Sony, he turned over the phone numbers of senior executives at each studio, and invited the journalists to check for themselves the studios' loyalties right then and there, no matter the time differences, with a telephone call to Hollywood. They did – and, says Kadoya gleefully, Philips and Sony suffered the embarrassment of piercingly direct questions from the press when they did hold the introduction in Tokyo in December.

At any rate, at last Toshiba had its alliance. Philips and Sony made a strong appeal to the computer industry, where it was widely understood the optical disk was the next peripheral due to be installed in computers at the factory. There were apparent initial successes. Skirmishing in the press went on. At last the tide began to swing when Toshiba agreed that, instead of a two-sided disk, it would adopt a technology from Matsushita which used a visibly clear glue to bond the two 0.6-mm disks together facing the same side – so that dual readers, or a flippable reader mechanism, were not necessary and the DVD could yield 9 gigabytes of recording capacity on a single side.

By the spring of 1995, rather than face a shattering format war on the world markets, both sides began to quietly confer in an assemblage called the Computer Technical Working Group. They were discussing a common format, and in August Sony proposed that the differences might be ironed out.

At that point the Toshiba executive who had been overseeing this tortuous warfare – a man named Taizo Nishimuro, who is today the chairman of Toshiba – decided that diplomacy could yield the much-sought peace treaty.

Between 14 and 18 August, Nishimuro made several incognito trips to the executive offices of Sony, a few kilometers away: it was the traditional summer holiday season in Japan, and it seemed like an opportunity to talk face-to-face without attracting public attention.

There was a lot to talk about, but unfortunately the diplomacy seemed to be headed for failure and in fact the talks seemed to have broken off, when both sides made an extra effort to override mutual misgivings and try for a deal.

But over what, precisely, could they reconcile? It turned out that there was one last, technical detail Sony wanted granted in the designs, and if that could be accepted Philips and Sony would come over. The world would have a unified standard, backed by a DVD Forum with all the industry's most influential hardware and software makers in its ranks.

And Toshiba would collect quite handsome royalty checks.

Ah, details. It turned out Sony wanted to substitute its own circuitry design, for a different system of signal modulation. Some people thought it might be reasonable, some thought Sony was trying to save what face it could from its defeat. "I sensed that if we took some important specification from the Sony design, Sony would finally agree to our standard," says Chairman Nishimuro now. "They wanted some symbolic thing. But our own camp was very difficult to be convinced then, and everyone had to be in agreement on everything. Our camp insisted that this was a total system, and they didn't want to break it apart now."

This might be what the Japanese, if they had such a game, would have called high-stakes poker.

A way around the bluff on both sides was found when IBM, which had been influential in pointing out the good specs of the DVD system when applied to computers, was called on to mediate a final session of The Working Group, held in the neutral territory of Oahu, Hawaii.[3] While the counting of just how many angels could dance on the head of this pin seemed impeccable, "Actually," insists Nishimuro, "we had told them please find something we can use as a concession."

IBM pronounced in favor of the Sony modulation method.

Although Nishimuro reports that there were still DVD campers who wanted to hold out, by 15 September the war was over. A vote of the Toshiba allies was taken. Five agreed to accept the Sony change, two recorded against it. Nishimuro stopped the show. "I want you to vote again," the record says he said. "I want everyone here to agree to unify the DVD format. If any of you still do not agree, we should stop and think and discuss thoroughly again."

They did, for eight more hours. The addition of Sony's modulation method won unanimously, and "Members attending the press conference that night," one report said, "all seemed exhausted."

The format specifications were published 8 December 1995, some 15 years after Mister Yamada had gotten the idea he could build a better disk. Only one last roadblock remained. Sony declared that the code-name for Toshiba's format, SD, ought to be changed to something else. The Toshiba format members let out a collective sigh, one imagines.

And thus was DVD delivered unto a waiting world.

There are no fools in the ranks of Toshiba's competitors. The wild change-partner dancing of the companies backing first one, then the other, then back to the first, format was the result not of executive ego and hubris, but of a phenomenon the public that was the buying target didn't notice very much at the time: what the academics used to call "a paradigm shift." In the history of popular media, we first had paper as a memory device. Then came magnetic tape, followed by magnetic disk and solid state memory. Next up was optical memory – disks – based on the technology of the laser (DVD and CD both work by implanting long series of tiny pits in the disk's plastic surface. The laser reads the pit-and-space combinations as ones and zeros, thus making them into a code that controllers and computers can read).

When the generations of technology necessary to make a true digital disk aligned – which is what Yamada had awaited – everyone in the game realized that whoever could establish the common format could patent it – and could "own" the next generation of memory medium.

Toshiba, the winner, today is the core of a group of patent-holding firms that earns royalties of several dollars per unit on global drive sales that are running about 100 million sets per year, and a few cents on each piece of software, that's selling from 300 to 500 million pieces per year. This is an alliance that has built for Toshiba a revenue stream that will bring it, both from product sales and from patent royalties, many hundreds of millions of dollars over the coming decade, a cash flow to support a company as big as Toshiba through bad times and good.

Fighting to command the standard was fighting for treasure, pure and simple.

Second, the competing standards proposed were all essentially based on the same principles: pits, plastic, and lasers. It was in the details of the technology that they differed. So, the engineering capability of making a product like this by no means belongs to Toshiba alone. All of its competitors command tremendous technological resources, and stand ready to invest in more.

But – they all understand the principle of today's distribution environments equally well: speed-to-market makes it very dicey to insist on building your own product in every detail, because a competing partnership could get there first. And, obviously, without movies you cannot sell a movie player: Hollywood was looking for a product, a format it could adopt in unison that gave it all it wanted in quality, pricing, encryption, etc.

To waste time by holding out meant to risk the format battle choice would fall into the hands of the studios, not the hardware makers (in fact, Toshiba managed to win partly because it managed to align several big studios behind DVD).

But not all makers are equally strong at all things. Toshiba knew its format backers would have to be persuaded to placate Sony and bring it into the fold, because Sony is feared in the industry as much for its marketing power as for its manufacturing prowess. If Sony were to insist on its own format no matter what, consumers would be drawn to it simply for the name.

As Yamada puts it today, "The actual thing is that Toshiba is not so good at selling these things. Toshiba invents, but doesn't make good sales, and always Sony takes over the invention and runs away with the marketing. And right after them is Matsushita." Confusion and spoliation of profit plans would have reigned, in other words. For everybody, including the consumer.

Eventually, then, the "alliance" argument boiled down to deciding how to slice the pie for everyone.

Hase is content with the way DVD has been selling so far: "The US market is split between Sony, RCA (owned by Thomson of France), Panasonic, and Toshiba, more or less with 20% each." One big US newspaper forecast DVD would be in a quarter of all American households by the end of 2001.[4]

But he's content for more reasons than that. "The entertainment side of DVD was not the final objective of Toshiba's development effort. It was one of the important elements – but our truthful motivation is to go for a new computer-storage medium. If you remember, we had a great business in CD-ROM drives for just this purpose. Today we are supplying, I don't know, around 30 million drives a year – 25% of the global market.

"So our main focus has been, how to migrate from CD-ROM drives in computers to DVD-ROM drives, and capture even a larger share of those component suppliers – IBM or whoever. Let's do it! And we're doing exactly that. Our sales of DVD-

ROM drives compared to DVD video drives are probably seven to three."

Quite a new-product sales drive, by any count.

NOTES

1. "Video Warfare: How Toshiba Took The High Ground," *Business Week*, New York, 20 February 1995
2. "Video Warfare: How Toshiba Took The High Ground."
3. "Toshiba SD Emerges as Next-Generation CD Standard," *Optical Memory News*, 26 September 1995
4. "Beyond the VCR," *USA Today*, quoted in *Southwest Airlines Spirit* Magazine, September 2001

CHAPTER SIXTEEN
RESEARCH & DEVELOPMENT:
A WAY OF CORPORATE LIFE

Without fanfare or formality, it suddenly appeared one morning in the lobby of Toshiba's enormous headquarters tower in Tokyo. Over by the elevator banks, on a card-table draped in white, sat a small trophy with a certificate that modestly announced it to be "The Imperial Invention Prize." By special consideration of the Imperial Household, awarded to Toshiba for the "Giant Magnetoresistive Head for Realizing High-capacity HDD" by the Japan Institute of Invention and Innovation as the most prestigious recognition of engineering creativity in all of Japan.

By the time Toshiba's 8,000 Shibaura staffers were streaming back out the doors, at the end of the day, the table was gone. That's all there was to it.

The new age of disk drives – an entire library in the palm of your hand – had just been launched.

It was the bisection between a 1991 evening and night when Masashi Sahashi, 42-year-old head of development for magnetic materials at the Toshiba Corporate R&D Center, emerged from his office and let himself fall into one of the easy chairs of the "upstairs club" in the main lab building, to order a beer.

Pouring it out slowly, as transfixed by the golden bubbles as if they were the rarest of tropical fish, he let his thoughts flip from the day's work back to the idea that had been teasing at him for days.

He didn't notice his friend Tetsuhiko Mizoguchi was even in the room, until the latter slipped into the opposite chair.

"You know," said Sahashi, leaning forward to pour a second glass for his colleague, "there's no damn reason in the world we can't do it."

"Do what?" said Mizoguchi, saluting him with a perfunctory toast. "You mean the magneto-resist head we've been talking about?"

"Yep. I've been thinking about that paper in the *Physical Review*. I think the principle is a sound one, don't you? We've got a great magnetic materials lab here, and a real challenge to catch up to and move ahead of the opposition. There's no reason why we shouldn't investigate this principle further – maybe sandwich layers *are* the best path to a Giant Magnetoresistance effect. If we can make it work . . ."

If they could make it work, Sahashi sensed, then they could achieve the incipient promise that exotic cobalt alloys, arranged in layers, offered: at least a 20% magneto-resist ratio, where IBM's new disk-drive head technology, which had shaken the industry, was achieving only 1%.

They could increase the sensitivity of a hard-disk-drive pickup exponentially, that is – load dozens more gigabytes of data on every square inch of disk surface, cutting cost and exploding the capacity of memory not only for computers, but IT devices of all kinds.

It was just an idea. But Sahashi loved to talk it over with his friends – at tea break, at lunch, after work, over beers in the upstairs club. They had all begun reading on the subject of next-generation head technology, and they knew they would have to pick a place to start somewhere. Gradually, more and more, they started to think this German university research paper really showed promise. But they kept it under the table.

★

Most people think of research and development laboratories, perhaps, as antiseptic rooms banked with exotic equipment and staffed with somewhat grayish people in whitish smocks. It may be a true enough image for a pharmaceuticals lab, but would be a very misleading way to picture the R&D establishment that will spend some 1.2 trillion yen between now and 2003 delivering new technologies, new competencies, and new products to the Toshiba group of companies.

R&D is not just a contributory function to Toshiba's work as a manufacturer. It is, rather, what Toshiba actually does – the most important thing it does. All the products, and product concepts, and gathering of these into businesses for Toshiba and translation into profits, are in a sense incidental to the work of conceiving, blending, polishing, and producing new technologies – and then renewing them and expanding them and crossbreeding them, on and on.

It is where the Voice of the Customer, as Toshiba refers to marketplace demand, preference, and potentials, meets R&D that Toshiba performs this key function. R&D is stretched out all through the corporation like the walls that define a medieval city, with manufacturing lines adjacent on the inside and the marketplace spread all round the outside. Every desire the market expresses, and every response the manufacturing operation produces, crosses back and forth through the myriad gates in that wall.

R&D is the primal function of Toshiba because it produces knowledge of a kind and sharpness no competitor of Toshiba's quite has. "While information may be free or nearly so," writes Dr. W. Mark Fruin in *Knowledge Works*, his study of "Managing Intellectual Capital at Toshiba" (Oxford University Press, 1997), "organizational learning and knowledge are not." Toshiba's huge investments are to convert information into knowledge and then to experience, which together produce the products.

Because this knowledge and experience are injected not only into the ideas for products and improvements, but into the products themselves and the ways they are made, the structure and flows of R&D work at Toshiba are not confined only to "labs," but permeate the organization:

- The Corporate Research and Development Center, 1,000 researchers strong, is responsible for fundamental research, out along the frontiers of science and engineering, to bring in and put basic shape to the breakthroughs that will become Toshiba's new businesses five or ten years from now.

- Each of the in-house companies has its own development center, where technologies (whether produced by Toshiba or not) are refined for the creation of products and manufacturing techniques that will be ready for market in three to five years. To oversee these centers, Toshiba uses a unique management structure inside each in-house company: each has a chief technology executive, besides a company president, and under him a staff of technology executives who supervise R&D work as well as cooperate and keep in touch with the other labs in the corporation, for cross-pollination of technologies in the garden of Toshiba's new-product concepts.

- Each of Toshiba's plants is aligned with one or more of the in-house companies. And each plant has its own engineering department on the site. These are the engineers who design what will be the finished products, improve them, adjust production technologies and systems to get them made and shipped. The designing that translates engineering technology into products, then, is all done right inside the factory, virtually right next to the production line itself. In fact, many plants have more engineers assigned than workers.

Often enough, an engineer's career with Toshiba will follow this path: from helping perfect the basic principles of a technology as a "pure researcher" at the R&D center, to a transfer to the in-house company development center who will use the technology to make product concepts, to a transfer to the plant, to oversee the installation of the technology in the engineering offices where it will be transferred into actual product designs.

It might be useful to see this organization as a pipeline system, in which all the technological competencies are circulating through the whole Toshiba structure. New ones are added periodically from the R&D Center, and are refined periodically into higher and higher grades in the development centers of the in-house companies and in the plant engineering departments. This pipeline can be tapped anywhere in the system where an actual product is under development.

The most important factor governing the flow is not pure technological mastery, however. It is the Voice of the Customer. Toshiba's marketing job is to be close enough to the customer to know what he or she wants almost as fast as the customer himself knows. Then turn to the pipeline, draw out the necessary technologies to make the product quickly, and bring it to market.

No manufacturer can hope to present the right product at the very instant the customer recognizes his or her need for it, of course – but the more sophisticated the technologies within the pipeline, circulating to every branch of Toshiba, the faster they can be tapped, and converted to products, right at the plant level. Proceeding from this pipeline structure is the second key concept to success, right behind Voice of the Customer: speed-to-market.

How much money you can make from knowing what the customer wants depends on how fast you can put that thing in his or her hands. That's why the R&D engineers who design the products sit only meters away from the plant workers who make them. That is why through 2001 Toshiba was preparing to marshal 3,000 engineers – triple the number staffing the

Corporate R&D center itself – of a dozen different disciplines, cutting across the lines of three different in-house companies, just within the Ome plant, to focus on digital, mobile and network products.

Every second counts.

Masashi Sahashi, the magnetic materials expert, and his colleague Tetsuhiko Mizoguchi were making definite, if slow, progress. In line with the physics papers they were consulting, they had advanced their idea of a hyper-sensitive hard-disk drive pickup and writing head to the simple concept of a multi-layer sandwich construction of almost microscopic proportions. And they had layered several different alloys and thicknesses of cobalt–iron, interspaced with copper, and tested them. But major problems remained. There was too large an insensitivity to hysteresis, another way of saying that areas of very light magnetism on the disk could not always be read by the new materials.

Six more people had joined the team – and under the rules of under-the-table research, formalized by Toshiba as the Young Researcher's Initiative, in which Center resources and ten per-cent of an engineer's time could be used to pursue a personal technological inspiration of the "young researcher," Sahashi had presented many proposals to formalize the project as an official undertaking of the whole R&D Center. Those proposals had been turned down repeatedly.

So over and over, it had been back under the table with it all.

But now, in 1992, the center's director could sense Sahashi was on to something with real promise. Thirty researchers volun-teered to take on the project from all directions – magnetic materials, materials processing, video recording head specialists. This itself was new to the Center's procedures. Normally research moved along a chain, point-to-point: this time the subject was being besieged from all sides simultaneously.

The siege soon began to prove effective. It was also in 1992 that Sahashi's team settled on the optimum mix of cobalt with iron, interlaid with copper, and the right thickness of each layer: 10 nanometers, or one one-hundred-thousandth of a millimeter. Still, the hysteresis problem haunted them – there was not enough sensitivity. Then they cracked it: the problem was not what they were making, but how they were making it. The solution to weak hysteresis performance in the cobalt alloy lay in the alloy's being given the right crystalline structure when it was laid down by a sputtering machine, so that orientation of the molecules themselves achieved an acceptable sensitivity to low-level magnetism in the data – and the head would work.

Since the introduction of IBM's MR head in 1992, the capacities in storage achieved per square inch of disk surface had been doubling each year. When Toshiba finally introduced its GMR (Giant Magnetoresistance) head technology to the market six years later, in 1998, disk capacity began rising by ten times every year.

The economics of the technology were revolutionized. Where it had cost 400 yen per megabyte for the equipment to store data bits on a hard disk in 1990, thanks to GMR the price per megabyte will fall to one-half of one yen by 2002. More space available on a disk – ten gigabits per square inch in 2000 – meant disk drives could be virtually miniaturized: made so small they could be built into a hand-held cell phone.

They are now approaching such capacity that, built into a digital TV, they could possibly store every program shown every minute of the day on every channel for a week, to be instantly played back by search access just like a computer's. Enter, for example, the name "Agassi" on Sunday evening, and sit back while your television finds and offers to show any or every televised match the tennis player fought during the entire week.

By 2000 the world of hard-disk-drive manufacturers had

abandoned MR completely for GMR; survey data collected by Toshiba shows the total world market for GMR-equipped hard-disk drives in 2005 will total ten trillion yen, or two and a half times the amount it was worth in 2000.

And that, as we shall see below, is only the beginning.

CHAPTER SEVENTEEN
THE PHILOSOPHY OF CREATION

AN INTERVIEW WITH MAKOTO AZUMA, 56,
DIRECTOR OF TOSHIBA'S CORPORATE R&D CENTER

Author: DNA computing, the single-electron transistor, quantum cryptography, CO_2 pollution gases absorption through new chemical compounds – the work your researchers are doing here at the Center is so leading-edge that laymen might call it something far more than "engineering." How much pure science do you do here?

Azuma: You can break down our goals here by the years and purposes of our work. After World War II we simply needed to catch up to the world, and that process occupied us, really, until the middle of the 1980s. There wasn't anything really scientific about it. But then the needs of Japanese companies began to move to the developmental side. In Toshiba's case, in the 1980s we concentrated on becoming the front runner of the semiconductor industry. Of course, national projects sponsored by the government, such as the Ultra-Large Scale Integration semiconductor program, had a very big impact on our growth. However by 1987 we were at the top, the No. 2 chipmaker in the world. Toshiba needed to have newer and newer technologies in other fields, and so we needed to refocus then on the research and scientific fields. We're now once again reviewing our mission, by the way.

But in the common definition of science, for example as in astronomy or geology, we're not doing that consistently: the discipline or pursuit of scientific questions for many years, the grueling search for the solution of a single question for its own sake, is not followed. Even in our advanced work, like fine-line silicon etching, we still are practicing engineering.

In very complex fields of high technology, however, you could say we come very close. What we really do is use the principles developed by science, incorporate them into new frameworks, and learn how to use *them*.

Author: I notice something curious about your organization. Your research manning levels here, at a time when you have set goals for development of new strategic technologies, have declined by more than half since 1992. Why?

Azuma: That is in line with the company's new policy of strategic allocation of resources. We have lost numbers, but other echelons in the research structure gained them. For example, Toshiba now has ten in-house companies, each with its own development center where the direct support engineers are more specialized. We didn't have all those before.

These development centers are the focus of 20% of our total R&D effort now, but in two years the ratio will rise to 30%.

Right now, 58% of the work we do in this center is to support Toshiba's current and next-stage businesses. The remainder, about 42%, is research for next-generation technology.

By 2003, that ratio will change slightly to 60% for Toshiba business support and 40% for next-generation technology. Of the 60% ratio which will then be supporting Toshiba's business, only 30% will be devoted to current businesses and 30% will be spent on Toshiba's near-future businesses.

In other words, there is a clear shift in emphasis within our own house to development of near-future as opposed to current technology, and a slight cut for long-term basic research.

At the same time, however, the in-plant engineering departments are going from 38% of the whole program to 30%. So the corporation is not losing manpower anywhere, just moving its

THE PHILOSOPHY OF CREATION

human resources to the levels where demand for their skills, in terms of time-to-market, will be greatest.

Other factors enter into the balance, such as our ability to outsource certain technologies at the plant level, which lowers the need for design work in the engineering departments. There is also less reason for R&D Center researchers here to find new businesses for Toshiba, because each in-house company is targeted toward doing that on its own. At least in the near future.

Our job here at the center is still heavily focused on tracking the knowledge from pure science, knowledge that will become Toshiba's businesses in a decade. So we ourselves now do more and more fundamental research, of the type that Mori did on character recognition, and Sahashi on hard-disk drives. Their work could bring us whole generations of new technologies and new products, in new business fields. Mori's research on pattern recognition almost 30 years ago, for example, today gives us the business of voice recognition in electronic automobile navigation sets – more than 80% of that technology is Toshiba's.

Author: Intellectual properties, the fruits of all your work in the formal sense, make up a large treasury of viable assets for Toshiba, don't they?

Azuma: Oh, yes. There are 30 to 40 staff working on patent filings all the time. They've been rather stressed on this patent business, in fact. They're filing 8,000 to 9,000 per year now, counting all Toshiba's research work.

Author: What other key work do you do for Toshiba here at the Center?

Azuma: We are in charge of Toshiba's participation in the industry-wide technology standardization process. We took charge for the company. We have to do that, otherwise no other company or organization would do it for us.

Author: How has this been received by other, competing companies?

Azuma: Yes, sure, they're enthusiastic about it. Their parts will be listed too of course. In some of these research areas, working for agreements is very much important to this global standardization. It has to do with coding the parts, so that we can simply refer to each part's code in building up the system designs. It becomes very easy for the designers to build up their designs, for manufacturers who need parts and consumers who need a machine serviced, if you only have to refer to a number and everyone knows instantly what specifications, what actual part, is meant.

So as you see from the story of DVD, to have world standards for this product that all makers adhere to, and for which we, or in fact any of us, have the patent, this is an advantage to the patent-holder. What we at Toshiba are trying to do here is make sure our technology is reflected in the global standards for DVD or MPEG or Bluetooth. It's important for any company to get its so-called modular details, get their part of technology into the standards, because they've been spending years and resources on developing that. Once it's in the agreed standards, it's a real advantage.

Author: And a real stepping-stone to expanding your components business, obviously. Tell me, what is this "under-the-table" work that your engineers keep smiling about?

Azuma: The researchers, when they have some idea that comes to them but has nothing to do with the project they are assigned to, they can explore and test their theories so-called "under-the-table." That means they can dedicate about 10% of their time to it without accounting to anyone. We don't want our people to go stale, and we don't want to miss out on any of the really creative ideas they have. Some of our best work started this way.

If their work on this informal project gives them confidence it would be viable, they can bring it over to the Young Researcher's Initiative, a more formal construct for research work. It means they have permission to gather the relevant researchers to talk about it, to think about it, how to make it viable. They are given six months and the specific number of researchers to work on it would be seven. They will make some sort of design for a future research product. If they still feel confident of the idea's feasibility, they prepare a formal research proposal that goes directly to the top of the Center – to me. And if I agree, they can be authorized to begin formally.

It was under this Young Researcher's Initiative that Doctor Sahashi started what became the GMR disk-drive success story. Doctor Mori's work on language recognition – the speech synthesis technology for car navigation came from that. But car navigation in the future will mean that while driving you don't have to look at a screen: you can communicate with the car's system by voice – you will even be able to control the car by voice, by combinations with other technologies such as microwave, infrared, etc.

And then we need to design that in a smaller size, so that we can carry navigation systems with us, as we walk around, using voice recognition. Mountain bikers, boaters, hunters, snowboarders, and hikers could have the same kind of global positioning satellite-based navigation guidance that their cars have.

Anyway during the six months, the seven researchers work on their own time, after hours – extra time. Sometimes, yes, they do get together after business over drinks; it's why our restaurant serves beer and other beverages upstairs. Whatever works.

Author: You have 100% of budget control over the Center's activities?

Azuma: 100% of the expenses of this R&D center are paid by the corporation, as a matter of practice. I have authority to use

80% of the money, to finance our activities. But when a new business we develop is turned over to the relevant Toshiba group company, 20% of the costs of developing it are paid by that company. Or, if we can find no application for the technology inside Toshiba, we might license it outside the company. Our licensing income now is increasing drastically. Many directors before me have been making efforts to expand this revenue stream, as well.

The money is paid to Toshiba Corporation, of course, not directly to us. But it comes to several tens of millions of dollars each year. Much of this is the licensing of the production of our parts by our own supplier companies: we furnish them the license to make our proprietary product, and they sell the product back to us.

Author: So one way or another, your research is all viable in the world of business?

Azuma: If no one in the Toshiba family can develop it, we can form our own joint ventures to apply it. As an example, we have a venture business 60% Toshiba-owned and 40% Mitsubishi, operating here and operating in England. Not only might it return a good profit someday, but this option is very important to Toshiba researchers who need to believe that what they are investing their efforts in will be successfully commercialized some day.

InterDesign Technologies Inc. is the name of the venture. In the R&D Center we invented this kind of IT technology to support designers of software. It takes a long time and it costs very much to implement the specifications of the customers or the demands of customers into a completed, software-generated design of what will be a real product. So use of this tool makes it easy to apply faster what the customer wants added to the software, and designers don't have to go back to the first stage of development to do it. Our invention takes the design and makes a prototype on the computer screen, so that designer and customer can both see it immediately. It enables a short turn-around time, the customer can understand how it works, and we can get his approval on the spot.

We sell it to design studios, design offices that have client-service needs just like this, but no quick solution. In March of this year [2001] we started a company to sell VisualSpec, the actual product, together with the Mitsubishi trading company.

We also have a terahertz technology we spun off through Toshiba Research Europe Ltd. into TeraView Ltd. We are one of the shareholders. It's based at Cambridge University, and that school is another shareholder. The investment we made was in kind, of research workers, technology, and even fixed assets – laboratory equipment. In return we received shares. Its development project is medical imaging technology that, for example, would be useful to detect skin cancer. There is no good conventional technology to detect skin cancer now; much higher sensitivity is required.

As you know skin cancer is very serious in Western countries, and as you know the ozone hole conditions seem to be getting worse. This could be a product for its time.

Author: Let me ask you about your own philosophy as the chief researcher for Toshiba.

Azuma: I've been working in this center for 25 years. And I know its weak points as well as its strong points. The worst point is that too many people here don't really like change. So I adopted the slogan "challenge to change." As Churchill said, "To improve is to change; to be perfect is to change often." Japan today has lost ten years to more or less recessionary conditions. Toshiba too suffered through this decade. Doubts about Japan have arisen in these past ten years. So we must create value the way we used to, in Japan, Europe, the US, and Asia as well. The way to do this is to change. And to build on your strength!

There are a number of slogan keywords targeted at the executive staff in our R&D family. To sum up these principles there is a Japanese word one could use, *mekiki*. It translates into a virtuoso, a connoisseur, an expert judge. A mekiki can say, when a foal is born on a thoroughbred ranch, whether the horse will grow into a champion racer or not. For us it includes the concept of technology insight, foresight, assessment, even connoisseurship. Someone who knows what will pay off, the moment he sees it.

Author: So, you've been the head of this center for two years. Are your people changing?

Azuma: On average, more than 150 Management Innovation 2001 projects are going on all the time here now. Each project takes from three to four months. As MI projects these are meant to change existing inventions, not to initiate actual long-term research projects. My final goal here can be summarized as to raise the total market value of Toshiba Corporation, by adding value products to its achievements,

You can get some feel for how we are doing at that by seeing how the press has covered what we're accomplishing. We were already up to six press releases a month in the last six months of 2000. This is the kind of thing that investors notice; this is the kind of thing that has a beneficial impact on our share prices.

Author: At 56, you are somewhat young to be heading this large and important an organization for a conservative corporation. Age levels among researchers are an issue, as to whether older members still have the ability to be truly creative. At Toshiba, even in the in-house companies there is talk about that. What about your organization?

Azuma: Yes, there's something to that. Older researchers work for younger directors, it happens often here. It's a natural thing. Especially in the IT section. A senior manager is generally 42 to 43 years old, and that is very young. He may have team members in their 50s. But among my chief fellows, there are very famous researchers worldwide and they are ages 50s to 60s.

However in the main, for researchers doing the direct research work on IT projects, we try to keep that staff young. The average salary for a researcher in his late 30s or early 40s could be as high as ten million yen, depending on his or her title and on his or her research achievements.

Author: Do many people leave here for other jobs, or to teach?

Azuma: Not many. About ten people each year leave for other jobs, many in their 30s or 40s for teaching posts at the country's major universities. There were for example seven lecturers at the last LSI Symposium, and five of them used to work here. All are now university professors. Our own research staff has some relationship to the academies. In some cases, we establish a high-level collaborative research project. Whether we work here, or visit each other's labs to work, or collaborate by e-mail, or a mixture, it depends on what the work is and what stage it is in.

And this kind of collaboration goes on in our overseas R&D establishments as well, such as in England. And the same thing in China, where we are collaborating in R&D with professors, and that research is committed to the business directly.

Author: How many female researchers versus males do you have?

Azuma: 13 to 14% of our research staff are women. These are in positions from the very earliest entrants to two women who are in department-chief-class positions already. Another few are to be promoted to the same level soon. I have sensed that there has been a strange divide between male and female workers here, and I have investigated it carefully. Before, researchers were evaluated for their contributions over a 14- or 15-year period, and promotions were based on the results.

Women had lower ranks generally, I discovered, for two reasons – either there were very few women here that long ago, or they fell somewhat behind because they had left for maternity leave. So when we look at longer terms of service, female employees cannot be equally compared to males, and that is why so few seemed to have achieved higher rank. What's important to me is the ability of each at the present. So I have tried to stop rating females and males by long-term comparisons, but to look at the present stage of their contributions. So there is more equality in the comparisons now.

Author: When you were a boy, what was your favorite hobby?

Azuma: Painting. Watercolors. From the time I was three until I was seven, I used to paint every day.

Then I changed drastically, and spent all my spare time at sports.

CHAPTER EIGHTEEN
THE TOSHIBA FACTORY

A willingness to hold together the functional requirements for strategic [manufacturing] flexibility in the face of high capital investment requirements as well as high land and labor costs is remarkable, and that willingness distinguishes Toshiba from many Japanese and most Western rivals.

Knowledge Works: Managing Intellectual Capital at Toshiba
W. Mark Fruin

The table of organization at Toshiba's sprawling Ome manufacturing center is what's really the stunner.

If at all, you've come to imagine Japanese factories as cavernous buildings with long assembly lines, swarming with khakied young men air-gunning components together, or with white-uniformed young women probing electronic assemblies with soldering irons.

Then you are given the profile of Ome, probably Toshiba's most advanced production facility: 30 acres of land, 20 acres of plant. Staffed, on all shifts, by just 3,700 employees.

And the total of engineers numbered among those 3,700 is one-third *larger* than the actual production-line staff.

Three and a half billion dollars per year worth of product shipped annually, by a total of only 1,322 floor workers. What kind of a place *is* this Ome factory?

It is the quintessential Toshiba production center.[1] It may also be the quintessential model for a globe-girdling manufacturing enterprise strategy in the coming century. It is the place where the rubber, mounted on the four wheels of technology, design, innovation, and customer demand, meets the road to the marketplace.

Conceptually the Ome plant, which turns out Toshiba's portable computers, its hard-disk drives, computer servers, optical character recognition machinery, and portable DVD players, is almost a separate company by itself. Toshiba learned long ago, when Shoichi Saba steered the corporation in the direction of commitment to Information Technology products, that the business would be based on speed.

Time-to-market is the make-or-break here. Those competitors who get the new concepts out the door in product form first, win the margin game. Makers who try to follow on with copies, and then play catch-up with lower prices, are going to be at ever-growing disadvantage in the future of the IT world. There are no second acts here; the prize customers will almost all be gone by the time the understudy product hits the shelves.

What makes speed to market? Answering that question is what Ome really does.

Put briefly, Ome designs the products Toshiba wants to sell, improves the quality envisioned in the original concept, lowers the production cost by making strategic manufacturing choices, designs the production *system* that ensures both quality and economy, and forever strives to shorten lead time. It does just about everything, in other words, except selling the product.

All inside the factory.

And, it makes sure that what it learns in all these processes improves its own store of technological skills. What Ome really is doing amidst this is producing a factory, that can better and better produce the products of that factory. That's why, as Fruin's book notes, Toshiba at one time focussed 75% of its total corporate R&D staffing right at the factory level.

Sound confusing? After all, R&D engineers are supposed to be those people in white smocks working in slick and gleaming laboratories, aren't they?

Let's take a quick factory tour. The first place we go is not to the assembly floor, but to the engineering offices. An average of six new-model portable computers are ordered by the in-house Digital Media Network Company, one of Ome's clients, each year. From development initiation to delivery of the product, Ome's turn-around time on each will be six months – the fastest in the world.

Here on the engineering decks, to save time the work is parceled out among teams. Four men, or men and women, turn their attention just to the computer's casing. Using previous-model design software as a reference, they divide the job and the design into four separate and equal sections, so they can complete their parts of the work simultaneously, in a quarter of the time it would take if they all worked together on the whole project. Not only does the computer-aided design work include dimensions, composition, and analysis of strength and stress points of the proposed casing, but even the flows of injection-molded engineering plastic compounds are studied on-screen, to detect any weak spots the manufacturing work itself might accidentally build into the shell.

The guts of the computer are likewise divided up, among five engineers who will tackle such systems as power, disk-drive memory, microprocessor, peripherals and ports, etc. The work in both these sections should, to arrive at near-finished software for computer-aided manufacturing of the new units, take no more than two weeks before computer and case are married up.

Elsewhere in the building, some of the 60 procurement staff will have been notified to start consulting the lists of suppliers, whether for major components or for screws and washers, to see who supplies the best work the most reliably, for the best price. The General Manager of Ome Operations (in mid 2001, Junichi Iwata) and Senior Fellow Nobuyuki Takaki, among others, will make the decision on what to outsource and what to build in-house.

Toshiba knows that in every generation of computers, some parts will be standard, some exotic. The exotic and leading-edge components that make the computer truly new are almost always the things that Toshiba itself makes in-house – those are the parts that are value-added, even though these key Toshiba profit margins are buried inside the machine where the customer never sees them. The rest have become commodities, even among sophisticated parts, and are most likely supplied cheaper from outside vendors than from inside Toshiba, provided the quality is true.

Even for hard-disk drives, a true technological masterpiece of Toshiba, some parts are supplied from outside: in 2001 disks were made by Showa Denko or Hoya; the heads in all their ultra-thin layers came from TDK. Assembly into the final drive was done at Ome itself.

Altogether, on a product like a portable PC, more than 75% of the parts, from big to little, are supplied by Toshiba's family of vendors, which numbers 400, about half of them major corporations in their own right.

But there are other questions to be answered about cost, as well. Another engineering department is in charge of process, or the way the product will be made and the technologies needed on the lines. This is important because some new technique might cut costs – or costs might be cut by having the work done elsewhere, either more cheaply or closer to the customer. Or both.

Ome coordinates four separate overseas computer-assembly

plants of its own, in China, in Germany, the US, and in the Philippines. In the latter especially, labor costs are low and now many units for the American market are assembled there. (Here at Ome, new PCs are built for the domestic Japanese market.)

And parts supplies, if not cheap enough in Japan, can be procured overseas as well, for Ome or for the other four operations: vendors in China, the Philippines, Taiwan, in Singapore, and in Thailand are all used with some regularity. Electronic Manufacturing Service plants can supply assembly work as well: some hard-disk drives are now put together for Toshiba in China, for example, and the Philippines plant assembles 1,000,000 disk drives per month with parts supplied through Ome.

If this seems even more confusing than before, consider what was said above about Ome's most important product of all: the factory that makes the products. It has its own staff of 3,700, of which a large majority are design and development engineers, and the responsibility that goes with product innovation, quality parts procurement, cost cutting, faster time-to-market, better manufacturing process, control of four overseas manufacturing subsidiaries (and four domestic subsidiary operations), and three major Toshiba clients to whom it regularly supplies its wares: Digital Media Network Co., e-Solutions Co., and Mobile Communications Co. And then there are other makers who like to buy Toshiba's quality and have to be satisfied, too – Ome ships hard-disk drives to Apple, Compaq, IBM, Fujitsu, NEC, and to companies in China and Taiwan.

So with its home plants running now at 80 to 90% of capacity, and monthly and weekly and even daily production plans that can stop the lines anywhere, on a dime, lest over-inventories start to clog the carefully managed inventory supply chains, *and* let vendors upstream know when that happens so that excess inventory does not fall on its own receiving docks, Ome really needs to have its act together.

We may not be talking rocket science here – but definitely, computer science.

In the space of less than three years, to maintain the tremendous balancing act all these responsibilities, commitments, and echelons require, Ome has gone from simple office-automation style computer-control systems, through the family of Enterprise Resource Planning software acquired from abroad, to today's Digital Manufacturing and Digital Management.

Briefly, Toshiba has wedded, in the design section, computer-aided design, manufacture, test, and engineering systems with Product Data Management. Closer to the floor, it has joined collaborative engineering to purchase-sales inventory production, both again harnessed by Product Data Management to see that the right part is in the right place at the right time. And at the delivery end, it has married build-to-order and configure-to-order demands that allow for customizing products on the lines, to the weekly demand and supply-chain management and customer relationship management systems.

See? It's easy.

And it's still only just begun. Toshiba has decided that coming crops of new products will require an even larger community of engineering skills at Ome, drawing together from all over the enterprise specialists in audio-video, computers, communication, cameras, and memory cards, to tie together Toshiba's product-design competencies in a community of 3,000 engineers who will all report daily right here at Ome. That strategy was to begin to see realization in the year 2002.

It all makes the assembly lines at Ome seem as peaceful as a church. Out on the floor, standing in lines of five or nine, the workers move serenely but competently to put together portable computers like puzzles they know all too well, with boxes of numbered and ordered parts ready to plug and screw into the cases in perfect symmetry before them.

Today, the lines are discharging a new computer every 15 to 20 minutes.

The finished machines get quickly hooked up to a test harness for quality check before shipment – but not so quickly that one of the young men in khakis doesn't have time to banter with, and just plain grin at, a female colleague on the other side of his line.

No whirring air hammers, no smoky solder smells. Just one of the most efficient production facilities in the computer world. All running on brain power.

NOTE

1. For fuller explication of Toshiba's theories and practices of production, production management, labor relations, supplier reliance, etc., see W. Mark Fruin, *Knowledge Works: Managing Intellectual Capital at Toshiba*, Oxford University Press, Oxford and New York, 1997. As part of his research for his book, Professor Fruin spent a year actually working on the floor of one of Toshiba's factories.

CHAPTER NINETEEN
COME TOGETHER: e-SOLUTIONS

Assuming regulatory approval, retailers could sell food during a cookery programme or DIY [do-it-yourself] equipment during a home improvements show. Viewers might eventually be able to buy a dress worn by a soap [opera] star by clicking on the screen. Television operators, content providers and retailers share the spoils.

"Interactive Television"
Financial Times
5 September 2001

If only Sakae Yanagawa could turn his job into a television drama, people might begin to understand his problem.

"It's very hard for us to do business because traditionally Toshiba has been a manufacturing company," says the Chief Fellow of Toshiba's newest (since April 2001) in-house company and corporate concept, e-Solutions. "But our job is to sell clients ideas, or know-how, or experience. Something intangible – what we're selling is *our* people's talent."

So while the rest of 50-billion-dollar-per-year Toshiba sells stuff, Yanagawa has to sell ideas first.

But some are humdingers: You'll be reading about them someday in the rich, black ink of the Toshiba Annual Report.

Though its catalog lists 81 separate Main Businesses, Products, and Systems, from "microwave communications systems" to the exotic "project management service for system development" to the prosaic "solutions for the hotel industry," and numbers 44 subsidiaries and affiliates, there are really only four business areas Yanagawa and his e-Solutions colleagues have to worry about:

- Devising information management systems for 50 or 60 of Japan's largest corporate customers,
- Supplying similar designs and gear to Japan's e-Government System program, wherein the national management structure is attempting to fully digest the IT age,
- Intelligent transportation systems, by which your car will some night warn you that you're about to back into a fire hydrant you can't see, and
- TV commerce systems – the Big One. That's where Yanagawa has his foot in the door of the future, because Toshiba's had ideas about interactive TV for years and years. And the future is just about to begin.

Digital TV is a concept almost everyone has heard of. And heard of. And then some.

It's that tantalizing product of the future that seems always promised, never quite delivered. It means TV broadcasts and HDD or DVD recordings both will be ready for those truly big, hang-on-the-wall, 60-inch flat screens: perfect resolution, brightness, color-rendering in a format that will fill your room up like a movie theater. It's a great idea. It's already a reality.

And it's a subject that makes Toshiba people wince. After millions and millions of dollars spent perfecting the products, no one is buying them.

Well, not "no one," actually. Toshiba was first to market with a digital television set in Japan in the summer of 2000. Counting digital set-top boxes that convert a regular TV into one also capable of receiving digital signals, some 142,000 units were sold before year-end.

Then the market went slack, and by summer 2001 sales had

slowed so much Toshiba suspended production.[1] The reasons for loss of consumer interest seem to have been retail price and, perhaps more important, lack of enough satellite-broadcast original digital programming to justify the expense.

But far from losing faith, Toshiba was using the time to differentiate its model-market, cut prices, prepare more digital content of its own, and gear up for the launch of a new digital broadcast satellite service in the spring of 2002.

In October 2001 the company, along with Dentsu Inc. and Matsushita Electric Industrial Co., announced the formation of joint venture Viewpoint Communications Inc. That's a digital interactive subscriber service that will build platforms for advertisers to reach customers and to sell things via the new digital channels that are coming.

With 70% of the nation's televisions forecast to be digital units by 2010, and analog TV broadcasting to be completely replaced by digital in the same year,[2] the partners are betting the picture's going to get a lot brighter in a lot less time than it took for black-and-white TV to turn to color.

Toshiba, which does not wholly own a TV station of its own, is perhaps most enthusiastic about the coming conversion of the national television industry to digital because of all the *other* things TV will be doing besides showing programs. "Things are different here in Japan from, say, the US," explains Yanagawa. "There will be a whole new marketplace created along with digital broadcasts, through interactive digital TV."

"This is one business," agrees e-Solutions company president Hiroo Okuhara, "that we expect a lot of."

What both men allude to is that digital TV, though off to a slow start, is going to catch up fast, and it's going to catch up as a communications network, not just as program broadcasting. It is going to be designed from the start as a combination of telephone *and* television, to achieve in one step the kind of long-heralded dream of television interactive commerce that the *Financial Times* describes.

Here is how it will work: digital programming will be broadcast both by satellite and by ground transmitters. Every TV that can receive it will be hooked up as well to a telephone line. Some channels, or perhaps just some commercials played amongst the programming, will be accessible via an on-screen icon and a hand-held clicker.

You click the message that interests you, and the telephone in the TV automatically dials a data server center. That center, explains Okuhara, routes the call automatically from the phone line to the advertiser's own response center, whether by telephone or Internet. At that point, you're talking to the retailer or service provider directly, on your television screen.

Book a flight, a hotel, or a whole journey. Do your banking by electronic transfer. Ask for music samples; order the CD. Later on, you'll likely even be able to buy that sexy dress. How do you pay? A credit card with an integrated-circuit chip embedded in it is placed by you into the TV or its set-top box. The account number is read off the card automatically, and the amount is debited from your bank or credit account.

Now we see something more than simple TV – we see the outlines of vast networks of new markets. And that is where Toshiba, which also makes key broadcast-station and components and systems for digital TV and its marketing circuits, comes into the picture, or at least plans to.

"We can provide the whole circuit, and that is really the Toshiba product," says Okuhara gleefully. "Our first strength lies in the fact we already produce everything the TV studio needs, and we can provide everything it *will* need to make this new digital interface marketplace work."

Mmm – now we see the "solutions" strategy going to work. No matter whether the customer is a national TV network or a local station, the biggest carmaker or the smallest pizza- or sushi-delivery in the viewing area, Toshiba has all the parts and all the know-how to furnish the interactive connections tailor-made.

"Of course Toshiba Corp. makes the best digital TV sets," asserts Okuhara, "and set-top boxes and all the other things needed to make this work: telephone functions whether wired or wireless, service centers, computer processors and servers, all of it. Toshiba makes broadcast transmitters and tower equipment and electrical units and lighting sets and cameras and monitors and sound equipment and everything for the studio, for the news-gathering units – even a satellite.

"Where we come in, in e-Solutions, is where all of these have to be blended expertly into on-line, fully reliable systems.

"No one else can do all that together. Yes, a Sony can make tape-editing machines and a Panasonic might make cameras. There are many things we ourselves can supply from them, or from other makers, if a customer wants it that way. But those are only peripheral systems: the technology is all developed and products are all ready. Once you choose any of them, they all still have to be bound together into the seamless whole, a ready-to-operate total system. We're the ones who have the know-how and the other needed parts to do all that.

"But also, we'll be offering all the third parties here – the service providers and merchants who will reach the market through these systems – tested platforms, because we've been doing all this on a trial basis with analog networks for three years now. A bank, for instance, would want to sign up new depositors via interactive. We know exactly how to register that customer properly and easily over the TV connection. Only Toshiba can offer that kind of experience.

"Of course our competitors will quickly offer things like telephone-ready digital TVs, too. But Toshiba, again, has something extra to bring to the digital product: we're leaders in the computer technologies. We can install hard-disk drives, built-in programming recorders, in the TV itself that can record not just hours but days, of not just one but many channels. And then you search for retrieval just like you would on the Internet – by key word, icon, and hand-held clicker, for example, on-screen. Instantly, in microseconds, it's accessed and it's there."

It's there. Digital TV, the e-Market, the demand for ideas. So it turns out Mister Yanagawa and e-Solutions have lots and lots and lots of things to sell, really. Almost everything you could imagine.

NOTES

1. "Digital TV slow to take center stage," *Nikkei Weekly*, Tokyo, 4 June 2001
2. "Digital TV slow to take center stage."

CHAPTER TWENTY
TO YOUR HEALTH

You can thank Adamkiewicz for all the confusion.

And you can thank Toshiba Medical Systems for helping to clear it up.

The Artery of Adamkiewicz is the formal name for it, and the medical operation involving it used to be called – quite informally – the surgeon's Russian roulette. Because when the scalpel began moving around it, you had up to a 40% chance of coming out of the operating room paralyzed for life, from the waist down.

The Adamkiewicz artery is one of life's bad jokes. Inside your chest, beneath your heart, it has the job of taking blood from your aorta and distributing it down to the lowest part of your spine, where all the nerves run that control your legs and lower body functions. If the blood gets cut off, the nerves all die.

This can happen in the many thousands of patients each year who prove to have aneurisms: balloon-like weaknesses in the arterial walls, which could burst at almost any moment.

When the aneurism is in the lower aorta (the big vessel that ships blood all over your body from the heart down) itself, the fate of the little artery (1.3 millimeters wide or less) with the big job comes into play. Because the aorta has to be turned off for the aneurism and its deadly threat to be removed.

To fix the aneurism is a very delicate job that involves slipping in a temporary aorta, cutting some but not all of the 16 arteries it feeds blood to, and then hooking them to the temporary pipeline while the aneurism is dealt with and the aorta wall is repaired.

Koji Hase, then general manager of Toshiba Super Density Disc Business Division, played a leading role in the 1995 negotiations that led to the DVD format. He is shown here during a press conference on DVD standardization.

Taizo Nishimuro (*left*) announces the partnership that introduced DVD to the world. Warren Lieberfarb, president of Warner Home Video, is next to him, then Sony director Teruaki Aoki (September 1995).

Shoichi Saba initiated the first steps that made Toshiba a powerhouse in semiconductors and IT, but also took responsibility and resigned as chairman when a subsidiary disregarded COCOM export controls. Today he is advisor to the board, and honorary president of the Toshiba Philharmonic Orchestra and often joins its tours.

The company-sponsored Toshiba Philharmonic Orchestra is one of Japan's best known amateur orchestras. Employees practise on weekends for regular concerts and for its successful tours of the US and Europe. Here, it plays at New York's Carnegie Hall in 1996.

We won! School students from all over North America, from kindergarten to twelfth grade, participate in the Toshiba-sponsored ExploraVision Awards science contest. Toshiba seeks to encourage a love of science through ExploraVision and its sponsorship of the Science Vision Contest in Japan, the Students' and Teachers' Educational Materials Project Awards in the UK and the Shanghai PC Contest in China.

Taizo Nishimuro, Toshiba's chairman, stands on Tokyo Bay in the shadow of the Toshiba Building, recalling sailing from these same docks as a penniless student to take up a scholarship at the University of British Columbia.

Digital Broadcast System. The control room at WOWOW Inc., a
Japanese broadcasting company. Toshiba is the only company able to provide digital broadcasters with turnkey solutions covering all aspects of
transmission and value-added services, including TV-based e-commerce.

Toshiba's president Tadashi Okamura (*standing, left*) was recruited to
Toshiba by a former teammate on the University of Tokyo rugby squad.
Okamura played on the Toshiba Tamagawa Works team, pictured here.

Toshiba's president Tadashi Okamura and his wife Hiroko, snapped on the Great Wall during a 1997 holiday in China.

Toshiba is promoting its brand worldwide as FIFA's 'Official IT Partner' for the 2002 and 2006 World Cup tournaments. Tadashi Okamura (*left*) greets Joseph S. Blatter, the president of FIFA, Shunichiro Okano, president of the Japanese Football Association, and Michel Platini, former captain of the French national team and an advisor to Mr. Blatter, during a visit to Toshiba.

Tadashi Okamura, president and CEO of Toshiba Corporation: 'I ask all Toshiba men and women to communicate ideas with passion – because if you don't have passion and commitment to ideas yourself, how will others?'

But a surgeon, because of the necessity for speed imposed on him by the delicacy of this rerouting technique, never has enough time to cut and reattach all 16 arteries. Some are abandoned to save the important ones. That's the set-up for the bad joke.

The punch line is that the Adamkiewicz itself is attached to one of the 16 choices the surgeon must make – but he doesn't know which one! Why? Because in each patient, it's a different artery. He has to guess, because in most cases he simply cannot see the tiny Adamkiewicz.

And as many as four out of ten guesses prove wrong. The losers in this game of roulette leave in wheelchairs.

That's one – just one – of the kind of ticklish problems the engineers and doctor-consultants at Toshiba Medical Systems think about a lot. Toshiba makes diagnostic machines of five kinds: X-ray systems, computed tomography, ultrasound, magnetic resonance imaging, and nuclear medicine.

Anyone who's ever seen a CT or an MRI scan knows instinctively how complex the technology has grown. Computer speeds and downsizing, along with advances in applied physics, have made many of these machines as comparatively complex as space satellites: mapping the health "weather" in the most minute regions of the human body.

After ten years of research, Medical Systems engineers were able to marry another technological competency of Toshiba, imaging sensors, to the digital delicacy of computer processing and create a machine, the Aquilion, that operates with "multi-slice" computer tomography, to deliver the sharpest and most information-packed images of any part of the anatomy it is trained on.

"Multi-slice" describes the new scanning technique. The Aquilion scanner, mounted in a casing that looks like a huge donut, circles the patient's body on the platform within the donut's hole at one complete rotation every half a second, recording four parallel images simultaneously. Then a second go-round, at the same speed, gives four more "slices." When fed back onto a high-resolution digital computer screen, the result is a three-dimensional cross-section of the target area taken so quickly that natural body motion is virtually frozen, and the finest details emerge plainly.

The Aquilion has been on the market in Japan (where Medical Systems is the number one powerhouse in the diagnostic equipment field, supplying 50% of all CT scanners) for almost two years. Iwate Medical University, north of Tokyo, procured one. And in that school's Department of Radiology, Doctor Kunihiro Yoshioka had for some time been meditating on the bad joke of the Adamkiewicz Artery.

He was wondering if somehow MRI diagnostic technology could be used more efficiently, to show the artery to which the Adam-k vessel was attached in each patient, before aortic aneurism surgery. He had already published papers on the subject when he happened to read the specs of the university's new Toshiba Aquilion CT scanner – and momentarily forgot all about MRI.

"I felt this might be the real best machine to search for the Adamkiewicz." Beginning with patients who had normal aortas, he began snapping Aquilion CT pictures like a shutterbug, to see if the shy artery would emerge on high-definition digital scan.

It did.

"I spoke with one of the heart surgeons, who had positively identified the vessel in one surgical candidate, and asked if he would mind taking a CT scan to see if the results matched." They did.

Now, just in his own hospital, radiologist Yoshioka scans some 50 aneurism surgery patients a year before their operations – and finds the Adamkiewicz in 70% of them, using just the Aquilion. MRI picks up another 10%, and so now the surgeons' odds are eight out of ten, or better, on making the right connections under the knife. No one has emerged from aortal aneurism surgery at Iwate Hospital in a wheelchair for over a year now. "All over Japan," says Yoshioka, who attends seminars and meetings around the country, "hospital heart surgeons are talking about Adamkiewicz – it's a kind of boom now in the field."

And Toshiba? It's taken a quiet bow for the technology breakthrough, and gone on to forge a joint-research program partnership in mid 2001 with Johns Hopkins Medical Institutions of the US, to connect fluoroscopic scanning capability with a CT machine that will deliver 12 slices per second – meaning, if successful, the modified Aquilion will deliver images of injured or diseased areas of the body in motion.

The resulting instrument, it is hoped, will be capable of clinical use *during* medical procedures, to guide a physician's hands. "This means the clinician can guide needles, catheters, and other instruments with much greater precision," said Dr. Kieran Murphy, head of the team on the Hopkins side. "This in turn means a much shorter procedure time with less stress on the patient."

Medicine may be an art. Making high-tech diagnostic equipment is a business. Toshiba is number four in market share worldwide for diagnostics scanning equipment, which is its specialty, and number two for computed tomography scanners like the Aquilion. But is Masamichi Katsurada, president of Medical Systems Co., satisfied with business these days?

"Satisfied? No!" he roars. "You can't look at this as just a market for machines. We're very proud of our technology and our quality. But if it were just a market question, then that's all we would have to worry about: improving quality, improving accuracy.

"But the term is not 'market' – the term is 'health care.' Today customers in all countries are talking about cost containment, and full information utilization, and reducing extra expenses. So we must add an extra element to our products – IT, information technology, to bring more value or include cost savings."

Toshiba has done much to digitalize the enormous volumes of information that these diagnostic scanners generate, and so is as familiar, from its computer competence, with problems of storing, accessing, and mining information in low-cost ways as it is with looking inside arteries.

In fact, the diagnostic team of machines like ultrasound, CT, and MRI – all very expensive as stand-alone devices – are at another level very like information networks: they produce data which can be handled by computer and communication techniques, and can be stored the way computers store them and reuse them.

And therein lies a way to help the customer get more for his money.

"PACS – Picture Archiving Communications Systems," is the concept Toshiba has come up with, says Satoshi Tsunakawa, Senior Manager of Medical Systems' Business Strategic Planning Department. "It's what will be the next big market for us. Through data sharing, it can help any medical office or center cut costs."

The idea is based on at least two efficiencies in handling all the "pictures" these big scanners produce. If a patient is seen and diagnosed through, say, a Toshiba CT scanner at a Tokyo hospital, the images along with radiological analysis and even a physician's opinion and record of treatment can be stored together in a memory accessible through a server. If the same patient visits a hospital in Kyushu, hundreds of miles away, a year later with an acute complaint, the emergency room can summon all that data over telecomm lines, know the history of the case, take more images and compare them side by side on the same screen.

But that's going to be a way in the future, President Katsurada admits.

Right now PACS is aiming at getting more bang for the diagnostic buck by pooling small hospitals and clinics, which by themselves cannot afford such sophisticated equipment, into networks based on larger hospitals, where patients can be sent for diagnostic imaging. The images are then transferred digitally to a radiologist or specialist, perhaps one in another prefecture, and the resultant opinion moves back down the line digitally to the patient's original physician. The network can be used to assemble data, and from that data to generate on-line teams for expert opinions, booking of procedures, etc.

"I see it first off as a diagnostic center. The scanners and other equipment are all assembled, together with radiologists and good diagnosticians, who can interpret the information and transfer it back to general practitioners who sent the patients, or to specialists, or to anyone else who needs them. Later, the networks could grow. The government has already approved storage of medical records in digital form, so at the very least this will save any such centers the cost of X-ray films, or at least of storing them."

In the city of Nagoya, Toshiba has already invested money with a group of physicians to start such a center, with the hope of building the network out to reach smaller practitioners and specialists.

Of course, wherever business and the healing arts cross paths, there are practical versus professional considerations. Katsurada smiles. "Yes, it's a tough business. Every time the government starts talking about budgets, we could be affected. Very hard to forecast. And the nature of our business is capital-intensive.

"Because reliability counts for everything, half of our inventory – 180 million dollars' worth – is tied up in spare parts, all of them in 'readiness' positions around the world. We have a thousand service engineers just here in Japan, waiting for a phone call from some customer. Service alone is an IT field, an investment for us."

But while some competitors have announced they're leaving the field, Toshiba's technology is guarantee enough of survival, at home and most likely abroad. Medicine may be struggling to save money. But it will always struggle harder to save lives.

As long as Toshiba Medical Systems Co. can offer products that do both, the firm itself should remain healthy.

CHAPTER TWENTY-ONE
SOMETHING TO KEEP YOUR EYE ON

It catches you as off-guard as the sharpest mystery thriller in television.

Here's the plot: Toshiba is the third-largest television maker in Japan, collecting 3.5 billion dollars per year from its 5% worldwide market share.

Here's the mystery: Toshiba's not making any money at all in the television business – only breaking even.

And here's a clue as to why: worldwide growth in TV sales amounted to less than 3% between 2000 and 2001. In both America and Japan, sales of TVs actually fell over the same period.

"It's a tough market right now," admits Ginzo Yamazaki, executive vice-president of the Digital Media Network Co. and responsible for its Visual Media Network Division, which handles all Toshiba's television-set and related equipment manufacture and sales through 42 subsidiary companies around the world. "But we have plans to make it a lot bigger."

Indeed. "Big" is the word for the most profitable and fastest-growing product set in the whole line right now, the projection-screen TVs. Toshiba has the number one shares for these high-margin sets in Southeast Asia, in Europe, and in China, and is bidding to move from No. 2 to No. 1 in the United States by 2003. That achievement would give it more than an aggregated quarter of the global market in projection TVs, and undisputed world championship. By then, the US alone will be absorbing over two million of the big displays each year, Toshiba thinks.

But there's a lot more on the Visual Media plate right now, as well. Toshiba has just, in 2001, diverted all home production of its standard, cathode-ray-tube color TVs and digital TVs – half a million of them per year – to its subsidiary Dalian Toshiba Television Co. in China.

Toshiba has had operations there for five years, and the quality standards have risen so high that all of the company's product for the home market – including even its new digital television sets – is being made at Dalian.

China is one area where total television market demand is still exploding, and Toshiba furnishes about 2% of the market right now, in furious price competition with home-capitalized makers. But Yamazaki expects his share to go up by a full percentage point in 2003 – and in China, those are big numbers.

"This is just the first stage now," promises Toshiba Chairman Taizo Nishimuro. "We have expanded that plant to a million and a half units of capacity, and that means we'll be able to produce multi-brand sets in the same factory." What he is pointing to is the likelihood that Toshiba will undertake OEM contract production of sets for other sellers in Dalian in future.

Once digital TV begins to show its true potential, with expanded broadcasting of high-definition programming in the advanced nations, there will be a rush of TV branders who long ago stopped making their own sets – or never learned how to make digital-technology ones – to buy them from the few full-technology makers left in the world, Toshiba being one of these.

There are other big things on Toshiba's television horizon, too. Plasma display screens, the 50-inch flat models that hang or stand flat against the wall and make sports fans drool, were to be exported for the first time by Toshiba in the spring of 2002. Prices will make these a real luxury for the consumer market, but Toshiba has its eye on the next step down the technological road.

In 2001 Toshiba and Canon engineers were working jointly on a new, Surface Emission Display large-screen technology, and they hoped to be able to show it by early 2002. "We don't know yet how the production and sales will be organized," said Toshiba President Tadashi Okamura. "But we have decided to put together all technologies from both companies and to evenly share the profits. If successful, it should be far superior to the current plasma display in terms of cost competition and image sharpness. I've seen it, the 100-inch model, and it's very clear and sharp. It'll cost – what, maybe one million yen?"

A 100-inch flat-screen television receiver for, what, $8,300? Pretty hard evidence that Toshiba's getting ready for a brand-new game in the television market, where it will be playing for much more than a tie score.

CHAPTER TWENTY-TWO
TOSHIBA PEOPLE

There are 188,000 men and women employed by Toshiba around the world, a personnel force almost as large as the combined active-duty troop strength of Britain's Army, Royal Navy, and Royal Air Force.

What is it like to be one of them?

Of course it all depends. On where you work, on what your job is, on what the markets for your products are like – and on who you are.

Classically, such big, old-line firms as Toshiba hired their employees, whether engineering specialists, factory workers, or administrative cadets, in "classes" once a year after their graduation from university or high school, and kept them almost all their working lives. No one worried about layoffs, or health insurance, or pensions. Or about getting ahead, for most of his or her career: wages were based mostly on seniority, and competition for promotion didn't intensify until an employee had worked his or her way far up the ladder, where the next rungs grew scarcer and scarcer.

When a company like Toshiba filled its executive ranks, promotions to equal levels were all drawn from the same class, year by year, so that juniors never supervised seniors. And those who were passed over in the ever-narrowing squeeze up to the vice-presidencies simply retired – often to a second job, arranged by the corporation, to round out pension vestings.

That's the way it was. It isn't anymore.

Lifetime employment as a "traditional" administrative fixture in the Japanese labor market dates back not even as far as World War II. It was largely premised on two facts: the employer was obliged to educate the employee, over his entire career span, whether as a master machinist or as an international marketing specialist. In turn the employee was obliged to remain with the same employer, and thereby repay that investment, simply because quitting left no way to go on the career scale but down, to a smaller firm that paid less.

All the biggest companies hired the same way, meaning lateral, mid-career job shifts among them were nearly impossible. Almost all vacancies were filled from within. The personal pronouns referring to this work force are mainly masculine not because there are no women but because women used to be, for decades, expected to resign their jobs, whether technical or administrative, at marriage.

And any non-Japanese seen in the hallways of corporate head-quarters or the walkways of the factory floors at home were sure to be just visitors.

Now, there are layoffs even in the biggest firms. Salaries are being increasingly reformatted from seniority scales to merit bases. Promotions go to those who earn them. Including to women, who have now at Toshiba generous maternity-leave plans and the open possibility of working at the company for an entire career.

One of the "benefits" of incalculable value to all Toshiba employees, male and female, has been, at least until 2001 when layoffs and buyouts were finally announced, lifetime employ-ment. Toshiba shrinks from using the term but in effect, especially with white-collars, the job has until the turn of the millennium been a lifetime guarantee: do nothing to disgrace yourself, and you will remain on the payroll until retirement.

This has been more than patriarchal protectivism. Large Japanese employers have always hated the thought of losing professional staff, because there is no pool from which they can immediately draw an equally skilled, company-acculturated replacement. And they also hate the thought of seeing proprietary company knowledge walking out the door inside someone's head.

But those aren't the only reasons. A company as huge as Toshiba, with so many technological competencies and such a well-established strategy of moving engineering development specialists along with a product technology, from development lab on to the factory where the actual products will be realized (see Chapter 16), has a great deal more to lose when its specialists start thinking of jumping ship.

A major trend in the vertical electronics industries has been integration of skills into a single product line. Just one example is all the technologies that will have to go into Toshiba's development of interactive video broadcast and response networks in the age of digital television. They include video imaging, studio and broadcast technologies, wired and wireless communication, data storage and retrieval by server, optical and digital memories and interfaces, computers, household- and office-size network configuration, marketing specialties, and on and on.

As technical people – even marketing people, close to the developments in customer demand – become more senior, more experienced, and more transferred, they spread their expertise more widely around the company in general. It is much faster to solve an integration problem with people who have experienced it before in a different department, and who know generally where the solution is likely to lie, than it is to start researching the technology all over again.

Every such career employee, in other words, is felt to add still higher levels of attainment to each of Toshiba's competencies just by staying inside the company, moving from team to team. (This career pattern also provides, of course, a grand test of who shows the most prominent management skills, for decisions that must be made at merit-promotion time.)

This is a far cry from saying that every bookkeeper or records clerk on the payroll is special. But a company as big and diversified as Toshiba knows well that it is built of teams, performing teamwork. And that a readiness by everyone to perform over-time work on the spot helps keep the payroll down – sometimes by a lot. And of course, that the unspoken guarantee of con-tinuing employment each Toshiba person has been offered until now is very persuasive when people are asked to work three, four, perhaps five hours of after-work overtime on no notice, rather than saying "I have to take the kids to a baseball game – good night." One must always be careful to pull for the right team.

It's not so far in miles, but it's a great many assumptions away from the atmosphere at corporate headquarters when a visitor arrives at the Ome Operations, scheduled to become the chief beehive for Digital Media Network production and design in the immediate future. As well as a plant tour, the visitor has asked to take an hour out of the busy day of five "typical" employees to ask their own feelings about working at Toshiba, down where the hands get dirty from the type of work that has to be done.

Ome's managers graciously conceded the company's time – but made sure an administration staffer sat in on the talks, as well as someone from the firm's PR office at corporate headquarters.

This "typical" lineup chosen by Ome for the group interview is somewhat different from what could be expected at the normal Japanese factory: because of the huge complement of engineers assigned here, mainly working on design of new portable com-puters and components and design of their manufacturing process (see Chapter 18), only one assembly worker from the line is present. The rest are young technical workers assigned to the design teams.

The first question: "Do you all plan to spend your entire working career at Toshiba?"

Among the five there are three yeses, and two nos. (In terms of salary implications, Toshiba probably offers about average on the scale of its industry. Salary for a 50-year-old blue-collar career worker would average about seven million yen per year; for a white-collar college graduate almost twice that, and for an executive of the same age, about 23 million yen per year.)

Why no? The first respondent is a tall young man with bleach-blond hair: "I can't foresee ten or twenty years into the future," he says amiably. "I might want to go independent, do something on my own some day. I just can't say right now."

"My job is designing DynaBook portable computers," says the other "no," a little older and a bit more quiet. "It's a good product. But it's already been around for ten years. Will it still be here ten years from now? And if it isn't, and that product is my engineering specialty, will I still have a job here? I'd like to be transferred before that point. But it's not up to me."

The next question is quite simple – what's the working day like? A slightly older but still youthful engineer answers: "We arrive at around 8 a.m., though there is a flextime system that gives us leeway. On the early days, I'm out and gone by 5:30 – I like to play baseball with my friends. But some days I don't get to leave until 10:30 or 11. Just recently, for example," he says with no apparent resentment, "there's been an awful lot of overtime. Last month I logged 70 hours." In a 22-day work month, that of course averages more than three hours' overtime each day.

At the table's end sits the interview group's only female, a software developer. How's professional life for a woman at Ome? "I feel there's pretty even job opportunity for both sexes," she answers unhesitatingly. "Even my female seniors, who've gotten married, are still here working on their careers. In the division I'm in, the highest-ranking woman is a specialist." (Equating to a rank something like assistant Section Chief; Section Chief is the standard grade of middle management in Japanese corporations.)

The sole assembly-line worker has been with Toshiba for ten years, and is a proud new father. He likes to go home to his wife and his one-year-old at quitting time each day, but overtime sometimes catches up with him too. "It's about two hours a day, when it happens," he says. But his complaint is not vociferous: his commute is so ludicrously short for the Tokyo suburbs – 15 minutes – that it sets his coworkers to chuckling.

Actually, he turns out to be the union steward for his section of the "floor." "I represent anywhere from 30 to 50 of my colleagues out there," he says, admitting that he's rather indifferent to his present two-year term. "But some people like to do it [the union office] over and over again."

There isn't a great deal of extra work to it. Toshiba has had horrendous labor battles in the deep, distant past, but the union now, as with many unions in Japan in mid 2001, is quiescent and most deeply concerned with job security issues. "I wish there was more contact between the union and the individual workers, actually," he says. "Some of them have different ideas about annual vacations [now 24 paid days of leave per year], but unless they pass it on in some organized form to the union, nothing will change.

"My union assignment really mostly concerns just passing information from the union to each worker, and handing out union questionnaires to everybody. Maybe that helps some.

"Yeah, I've seen several people quit their jobs here over the past ten years. But I can't remember anyone who had a really big grievance. My impression was, they left because they found better opportunities."

The company now is working hard to install MI 2001 management systems, introducing Six Sigma organizational tools with which all of Toshiba must comply. Japanese factories are famous for Total Quality Control, Just-in-Time, and Quality Circles right down to the assembly-line level. So are the new programs making big changes at Ome now?

First engineer: "What do I think? At the moment, at my level, I don't know if it has a good performance record or not, but management is working hard to install it."

Second engineer: "What I do know about MI 2001 is that it's related to Six Sigma. My understanding of it is that it's kind of a small-group activity, to talk about improving products or making new developments or things like that."

Third engineer: "Around us, our own managers are pushing it pretty hard, but it makes the staff pretty busy because we've all got our own jobs to do and this just comes down on top of it all."

Female engineer: "In my case, I've attended some educational classes on it. At this moment it hasn't penetrated down to the worker level. They've set some of us to working on it, drawing up educational literature."

Line worker: "I know about the activity. But as yet it has nothing to do with my own job."

And merit pay – does it cause problems between peers when one gets a fatter bonus than another of equal rank and seniority?

"There is a level, or a kind of ranking, to our bonuses," volunteers one of the men. "But personally, I don't even notice the difference between any of us. My colleagues never talk about it, and I really think it's because there's not much difference in pay at the same rank."

Finally, the tape recorder is switched off and the little panel of five is asked to respond to an instant survey anonymously, by a show of hands.

First question: Do you think the Ome Operations management is doing a good job now?

One hand rises.

Second question: Do you think Toshiba Corporation is doing a good management job of the whole company now?

No hands are raised.

Third question: How many of you would want to see one of your own children, once they've grown up, come to work for Toshiba?

One hand is raised.

Last question: How many of you privately own Toshiba's stock?

No hands are raised.

THREE WOMEN OF TOSHIBA

Japanese women are falling further behind women in other countries in terms of being able to participate in economic and social activities and assume decision-making roles, according to a government white paper released Friday . . . It noted Japan ranks 41st out of 70 countries surveyed last year.

Kyodo News Report,
in the *Daily Yomiuri*
23 June 2001

University graduates made up the largest proportion of new female employees for the first time last year . . . A majority of women earning college degrees means companies will have to rapidly establish systems to draw upon the skills of more highly educated women . . .

Nikkei Weekly
25 June 2001

A majority of women recruits possessing college degrees as they enter the work force of Japan's large corporations, as the country falls further and further behind in finding a place for them at the table of top management, means that a massive, slow-motion collision is beginning to occur.

Demographics are pushing women ineluctably toward leadership responsibilities that Japanese males do not want to give them.

To more subjectively explore the complex gender boundaries inside Toshiba, a company that will live or die by its ability to attract the most talented and well-educated men and women of every year's crop of university graduates, three career-track Toshiba women agreed to sit down for a free-form interview about their thoughts on their own careers and experiences.

First is Mrs. N, a senior product manager in the international PC planning department. Second is Miss F, a specialist in the planning group, global development and production coordination division. And third is Miss S, a member of the headquarters group.

N: I joined the company in 1988 as a mathematics graduate, and since 1990 I've been in the portable PC business. For eleven years I've spent most of the time in engineering product planning, but I've also spent a few years in marketing and also e-business while I was in Toshiba America Information Systems.
Author: A career mostly in portable computers. Does it still interest you?
N: Yes. I think it's a very challenging market – there are new technologies every year and even though compared to a decade ago currently the market is stable, or rather without much growth, we've expanded our areas from just portable PCs to also things like other peripherals that we'll be announcing soon.

Author: How do you usually work on designs?

N: Currently I'm in the product planning and marketing department and we have a portable PC team – approximately a dozen people in headquarters doing the planning. And we have maybe 200 to 300 engineers at the plant and worldwide, actually. And we have about six different models that are in development and shipping now, so we have separate teams for each of them.

Author: You obviously like the work, and have many important responsibilities. But a decade in the same type of work – when can you expect to be reassigned?

N: Since I returned from Toshiba America Information Systems just this April, I hope to be in this position for at least a couple of years.

Author: Is that about the same tenure track as for your male colleagues?

N: Yes, actually I think I personally have been given the opportunity to take more positions and have more different experiences than the average.

Miss F: I joined Toshiba in 1990. I took my degree in sociology from Hitotsubashi University. And I was told first that I would be going to procurement, because they needed more people who could speak English. But once I joined, I started off in public communications. I spent the first five years doing domestic PR and then the next few years, international PR.

Author: How did you feel about Toshiba once inside?

F: I was very fortunate with my bosses. Especially in PR there were many female journalists and so on that I dealt with, and so I didn't really think that there is any [professional] difference between male and female; I never thought those kinds of things for eight years in PR. But then in Toshiba, if you're a college graduate, the first promotion you'll get is in your tenth year. And I'm in my twelfth year now. So in my tenth year I started to see my friends and my colleagues who entered at the same time being promoted or not promoted, and for the first time I started to think of those promotions as being related to being male or female. I think it's now more focused on the individual's ability however, because I also began to notice my male colleagues who were not promoted, as well as female. And females being promoted ahead of them. So from my point of view it turned out pretty fair in my days.

I remember years ago I was on a project, gathering the history of all our female engineers. And at that time there was only one chief specialist who was a woman, and 54 female deputy managers. But today there are tons of females who have been promoted. It has changed so much in the past few years.

Author: Have you been stationed overseas?

F: I was transferred to production planning three years ago and I had no knowledge about it. That's why I got sent on a training program to the Philippines. Our plant there is a small version of Ome, and it was more convenient for me to study production. They were doing computers there, and PC peripherals, and CD-ROMs and HDD memories. There are 3,500 employees there.

Author: How do you like the field?

F: I find it interesting. There're many kinds of production planning, but if I'm assigned to an actual manufacturing site, I think it's very interesting and I would like to continue. No matter where it is, I don't mind – and I told that to my boss as well. I'm not married, so there are no transfer problems.

S: I graduated Keio University, Environmental Information. I was actually first recruited by P&G, but their headquarters were in Kobe. So I would have to move there and stay a good long time, but my parents didn't agree to it. So I applied to a couple of electronics companies, including Toshiba. When I joined there was a big fair called Tomorrow 21. It was a corporate anniversary celebration for Toshiba's 120 years. I went there, and I saw all the future products of Toshiba and I was really amazed at the high levels of technology the company had. And I thought Toshiba is really a good company. I made up my mind to join it.

They didn't give me the job I had expected, in marketing. I was first appointed to the administration office, which is totally different. So I went to the Human Resources Div. and asked for a different assignment, because I knew that if you are appointed to the administration office you could be sent to Oita, Kyushu, or any other plant all over Japan. I joined Toshiba, as I said, because I wanted to stay in Tokyo. But I couldn't say too much about it, because I was accepted into the company with a university-graduate status, same as a man. So I couldn't say I didn't want to go to any place other than Tokyo.

Eventually, though, I was reassigned to work here in Tokyo, and now I have been in Toshiba for three years. They have told me I'll be in this job until 2003, another two years.

N: For some of the young people who are newly joining us, who don't really know exactly what they want to do, leaving it to fate is probably a good thing for them. But if that person has a specific thing that he or she wants to do, I would like to see that person placed in that position, and actually in our division we have been doing that – within our capacity.

Author: But in a fast-moving engineering company, isn't there some danger in anchoring one's career and experience in just one product group or technological field?

N: I personally would not enjoy the same job year after year. I would prefer to be a generalist. But we also need that kind of person, the specialist, especially technically – a specialist that can do that field of engineering. As a company we want both kinds of people.

Author: You see yourself spending a full career at Toshiba, even though you are married?

N: Yes, I am married now but I have no children. So I'm very happy with the way I've been able to juggle my home life with my work. We have worked it out through the years. I've actually lived in the US working for Toshiba America Information Systems by myself, separated from my husband for three years.

F: To be honest, I don't know about a full Toshiba career myself. I like this company, I like the people here. But then when I think about my career I have a different sense from S-san. When I had the recruiting interview, I asked to go to the Corporate Communications Office. Then I moved to production because I asked for it. So I have always gotten what I wanted in my eleven years in Toshiba. But then when I think about my career today, maybe I was too late to start in production. I have tried it for three years, and I sometimes think maybe I'm too late to catch up in the production area, and perhaps I really don't have much chance in Toshiba as a production planner.

My bosses tell me I still have the chance to catch up, but I am not very sure and these personnel things always change when your boss changes. You never know what will happen when the supervisor who made you a promise is gone from the job.

I am always open up to other companies, for taking a chance to change things. Yes, I am looking. I like this company, I like the people here, but I've always answered to the – we have interviews every year November with your boss, and there is a question will you stay with Toshiba? And I always answer I don't know, because I really don't know.

S: When I think of a career, I think continuing in one job for ten years is necessary, rather than changing jobs after three or four years. I would like to stay, but not in my present assignment. Because it's a headquarters staff job, and that means if I stay there I can be a specialist in Toshiba after about five or six years, but I can't be a specialist anywhere else in the industry.

Toshiba is a big company. So each division has its own culture.

So maybe if I was in another division, I might be happier and I might want to stay my whole career in Toshiba.

Author: F-san, would you take a buyout to retire from Toshiba?

F: I don't know. Maybe it's the generation gap: even though I'm saying that I'm open to other opportunities I always, when I had that kind of chance, I always thought about my bosses. It isn't loyalty to the company but to the people who nourished me. Actually I've had a few offers in the past few months [from other employers], things like double salary, and I want to say "take it." But I'm now in the middle of a big project and it will not end until this December and I just couldn't throw everything away and run out.

Author: N-san, would you take a better job elsewhere?

N: I would definitely consider it and carefully see what that job would offer me differently that I would not be able to achieve here. Job content, yes, would be as important as anything. Of course the pay would be important. But the job content is the most important.

S: If I stay in Toshiba, they'll probably send me to some marketing division next, and then send me back to a job like this.

Author: But you first said you wanted marketing, and you don't know that they'll send you back here for sure.

S: No. It really depends on what happens next. But I'm not thinking of staying with Toshiba for the rest of my life, I suppose. But I do want to say that I think there is no discrimination here against women at my age. And there's none with the promotions, when you're going up to specialist rank. But I think there is a little discrimination against women when you go up to chief specialist, the next stage. That's just my opinion.

Author: Speaking of the future, do you own any of Toshiba's stock?

S: Yes. I do.

CHAPTER TWENTY-THREE
THE CHANGING FACE
OF MANAGEMENT

"'When in Rome, do as the Romans do' is advice that applies just as well to being in France," says Alain Prénat, chief executive officer of Toshiba Systèmes (France) SA for more than 15 years.

Doing as his French customers do, in speedily adopting the newest and best technologies whether to business solutions or consumer products, has made Toshiba "a key player on the European market" – Toshiba has been No. 1 almost each of the past 15 years in portable computers, and in 2001 celebrated its one-million mark in computers sold in France.

But it's not only in the sense of quality, high technology, and keen marketing that Prénat, one of Toshiba's few major foreign subsidiary presidents who are native to their own business region, suggests that Toshiba must consider ever more carefully "doing what is done" locally. "Working in a dual cultural system is not always easy, and may create difficulties in communication and understanding," as Prénat observes. "I have been given a great autonomy to manage our French company during these last 15 years."

And that has, to restate the point, meant 15 years of success.

Toshiba, like most big Japanese enterprises, has no executives, at the corporate level or the in-house company level, that are not Japanese. Overseas, there are more and more local faces among top-level executives, but the question still remains: how to transfer the instincts and habits of Toshiba's brand of success across "dual cultures" to other, newer subsidiaries and other parts of the world. Toshiba needs a new "technology of management" as well as of new products.

The company has come to recognize this and realize it in recent years, particularly as Asian business has blossomed. The corporation began to give managerial courses to local staffers in Malaysia, Singapore, Thailand, the Philippines, and China in the mid 1990s, and now, with 16,800 local employees staffing 47 subsidiaries in nine Asian countries, gives the training to about twelve hundred persons per year.

Higher levels of management elsewhere are also being given attention, especially in Europe.

"We began our Pan-European management Program Level Two training in 1998," says Ichiro Takemura, a Chief Specialist in Toshiba's Executive Compensation and Planning Group.

"It's held once a year for senior managers with five years or more of experience with Toshiba. We want there to be a cross-cultural and international communications dimension to it, so we gather them all together at the same place and time. And that in a way is our real purpose: to disseminate awareness among everyone of how business planning runs for all of Europe, not just for their own countries.

"We want them to know what the next corporate mid-term business plan is, and how they fit into it. So trainers from Tokyo, sometimes division general managers, explain it to them. And in return, area representatives will give briefings on their own markets to their European colleagues. Also we want them to know not only their own businesses, but others': a person from the semiconductor side should know also about the portable PC business. That's how new customers are found."

The same kind of training has been scheduled to begin in the US as well, in 2001.

Takemura recognizes that, at least in some cases, it could be more efficient for the whole management structure of a Toshiba overseas subsidiary to be locally recruited.

But, "In my personal opinion, as long as Tokyo makes all the major business decisions it probably would not work – the local president or chief executive has to be a Toshiba man from Tokyo.

"In cases where the whole business can be done locally, where design, development, manufacturing, and sales can all be left in their hands, it should save us money to have a completely local command chain."

Not only could money be saved, but decisions crucial to speed-to-market could be made that much closer to the actual "Voice of the Customer," it seems.

And what about Toshiba's opinion? "It's gradually changing. Not in all businesses, but in some. Each in-house company controls its own set of subsidiaries, and will have to make up its own mind along the lines of most-likely paths to business success."

But both Takemura and Toshiba seem to be very high on the idea of giving both managerial and skills training in any local subsidiary that shows signs it can profit by it. "Especially in the Southeast Asia case, I think our programs are better than any of our competitors'. When we first started in 1996, we were the only ones to do it on an organized basis."

Takemura says Toshiba has relatively few work-force problems around the world, whether or not the employees are unionized. Pay scales are matched to local standards, and human-resources policies are also matched to the host-country practices, and open for all to inspect.

And how soon can we expect to see a French or a Chinese manager assigned to the headquarters tower in Tokyo?

Takemura smiles. "As a personal answer, I think we should do it. We should ask a subsidiary executive, if his or her skills are sufficient, if he or she would like a chance to work at corporate in Japan. So the assignment rotation [for the whole company] should really be global for everyone who qualifies, and that should include a tour in Japan [for non-Japanese employees].

"Unfortunately, to do that is not very easy, because in addition to professional skills such employees would have to have sufficient Japanese, including reading ability, plus at least some English, and also must be fully prepared in the sense of cross-cultural awareness.

"But this year, for the first time we did hold a global leadership forum here in Tokyo, with about 30 of our key employees from around the world. It was two-way communication: we spoke about business plans from our side, and they from their side. And on the final day our President Okamura spoke with them all, and each received a course-completion certificate. We're going to do more of those, and other programs like them, from now on."

Toshiba is like any other Japanese blue-chip firm. As with women, the glass ceiling is still definitely there for non-Japanese managers in Toshiba's ranks. But at least the headroom underneath it is growing: subsidiaries themselves are getting bigger. And the new in-house company organization puts more of Toshiba's top headquarters leadership in face-to-face contact with their subsidiary staff now than ever before. The realization that the customer out there, not the executive in Shibaura, is the ultimate boss should give the Toshiba man in the field much more of a say over the corporation's day-to-day decisions. No matter where the field is.

There's another kind of change wending through the executive hallways at Toshiba, as well. The horizontal, in-house company management organization was designed not only to put different product divisions' leadership teams closer to their own customers. It was also designed to make these teams individually responsible for their own business results. In the globally shadowed economic era of the early 2000s, the shift to executive responsibility for performance can be enough to unsettle even the most sanguine former members of the collective corporate leadership.

Any failures from now on will have names and addresses.

It's too early to tell what the major consequences are going to be for Toshiba – it would hardly be fair, for example, to hold a semiconductor company president or general manager responsible in 2001 for faltering Toshiba revenues in the wounded DRAM industry, especially if they were handed their briefs not two years before.

But not all of the reorganizing has gone on at the corporate level. Below Olympia, middle management has traded roles too, and while results are not too much more clear there, some impressive stories of reinvigoration, such as that of Masaaki Nose and the 600 Toshiba employees who created a successful new sales subsidiary for industrial equipment (see Chapter Five), and a welcome to many of the changes, are heard clearly.

PART THREE

CHAPTER TWENTY-FOUR
THE EXECUTIVE FLOOR

When Yasuo Morimoto was 27, he found himself staring down a shotgun barrel, tracking pigeons, pulling the trigger – and discovering he wasn't very good at it. He still remembers all those misses.

Morimoto, today Toshiba's Corporate Senior Executive Vice-President, a director, and operational chief of strategic planning for the whole corporation, was taking a master's in applied mathematics at Cornell University in Ithaca, NY, the hometown of a famous long-gun maker. It was at the local country club that someone introduced him to a favorite regional sport, trap shooting – of clay pigeons – and he realized just how near-sighted he was.

All the pigeons may have gotten away that day. But as it turned out, having acute focus on the near-at-hand has proven quite an important attribute of Morimoto's management skills inside Toshiba. His job now is tracking results and conditions in all parts of the company – a set of moving targets if ever there was one – and keeping a close eye on the bottom lines of every one of the in-house companies and every one of Toshiba's more than 800 subsidiaries, affiliates, overseas offices, and joint ventures and business alliances.

He is the one who has to recommend to his executive colleagues what to do next, for or with each of them, to heighten its success, to reorient its strategy – or to get rid of it.

Not only of course does Toshiba make and sell microchips,

computers, satellites, locomotives, electrical generators, rice cookers, DVD players, refrigerators, and mobile communication systems: it has thousands of other products, split among dozens of other industries and product fields that are either maturing, blossoming, or just languishing.

Almost any one of them could be a winning generation of new products for Toshiba – or a crippling drag on profits or cash flow.

In an interview in his office on the executive floor in midsummer 2001, Morimoto looked out across the vast Tokyo metropolis and gave this thumbnail but thoughtful summation of the likely futures – or lack of them – of this panoply of Toshiba's assets and operations.

Author: Your corporate video "This is Toshiba" described a number of things that together add up to all Toshiba's business fields. Along with the main-scale businesses of Toshiba, they have all gone through restudy and planning for restructuring, with the help of analysis from consultants. Or *was* it helpful?

Morimoto: I think it was very helpful, a good thing for us to do now.

Author: So as I go through these, tell me what the profitability potential is now – low, medium, or high? First is Information Services – here, specifically cell phones. It's an extremely competitive field, and it shows every sign of changing quickly to a commodity product.

Morimoto: Of course this is a very competitive arena, but we are focusing on the 3G product, not the current generation of products where we are far behind competitors. But we have many core skills to blend into the product family, such as System LSI technologies for baseband LSI, and then many discrete devices. And also we have LCD and also we have MPEG-4 and also maybe some of the very useful, valuable new skills for the 3G terminals. So in that sense our target is to become one of the top three companies in the world, but in the Third Generation which is now about to launch.

Author: Then it can become one of Toshiba's highest-yielding businesses for the foreseeable future?

Morimoto: Yes, I think so.

Author: Bluetooth is a wireless communication command technology, interfacing with many kinds of devices over short areas. Toshiba is heavily involved with it.

Morimoto: I think both Bluetooth and MPEG-4 [digital data compression technology, used for sending video data through wireless transmission] will come to the market in volume at the end of 2002. So it's still early. Of course trial machines and mock-up machines and demo machines are all finished, but the actual market won't even open until the second half of next year.

Author: For Bluetooth to work universally, you need not only broadband, but also response technology to receive the commands. For example in the kitchen, there must be a terminal device to execute the command given to the microwave, or the dishwasher, or whatever. Can installing all those high-tech controllers be done profitably?

Morimoto: Oh, I don't think it takes a long time to do that, once people understand the product. Those kinds of applications should be realized and ready by 2005.

Author: What future do you see for Toshiba in digital broadcasting?

Morimoto: Definitely there is a monster market coming. We already offer digital television receivers for sale, and some broadcasters have digital programs on the air at various times. But the problem is content. It doesn't seem to interest viewers very much yet.

Author: Without a content market, how far can you stretch popular demand for the hardware?

Morimoto: That is the problem, because SkyPerfect TV or WOWOW [Japanese satellite broadcasters] or some other kind of digital broadcast system, they've got maybe one and a half or two million subscribers each now. In WOWOW's case it took almost ten years for them to get two million subscribers, and it's just started to break even for them as a business. Your question is a tough one. To make money in that kind of business, in the sense of simple digital TV broadcasting or some other case like interactive digital TV, it's going to take a lot more time. Even currently, neither WOWOW nor SkyPerfect TV has prepared adequate programming for digital TV – so content will be our major problem.

Author: So this business is a question mark?

Morimoto: Of course we have question marks. But even so, the direction of the industry itself – maybe it will take another three years to really open up. But the momentum is there, even if it's later than 2004. There's just no question that digital TV is coming, big-time.

Author: How about system integration business? It's a very crowded field now.

Morimoto: Yes, but it's going to grow for us. On the surface, it does present certain problems. So-called side businesses, just providing the hardware, is very low-margin. Everybody in the business is facing some difficulty in trying to create reasonable profits. But you have to look at the potentials in a different light. The package-software system solution business we are going to be doing is a kind of consulting business. We don't write exotic software ourselves, for huge operations. The software itself is here, it already exists: it's packaged software. But the customer needs to have it installed to suit his own applications, his own business. So we have to modify it for him, give him the whole system. That service is where the margins lie. It's the most flexible way to meet the current necessity for IT-based management.

Author: That brings us to another kind of software, of the Internet services type, like Toshiba iValue Creation Company's *Eki-mae Tanken* Club guide to the shopping, dining, entertainment, and major-building addresses around each railroad station in the region. It can be dialed up on a cell phone, and it can give you lots of useful information – but can it be a big money-maker?

Morimoto: I don't think so.

Author: Then why stay in the business?

Morimoto: Currently it's a very difficult type of business, not only for Toshiba but for the bigger guys. Fujitsu's Niftyserve or NEC's Biglobe [Internet search engines], looking at advertisement income, are growing in profits about a one-hundredth over these past two years. And soon Yahoo Japan will introduce a new pricing scheme. Pretty soon everybody who is an Internet line server won't have any profits at all anymore. It's just a very difficult environment.

Author: So you feel this business presents a special challenge?

Morimoto: Yes, a challenge.

Author: Once again, this business of entertainment content – say, making movies. Matsushita and Sony learned a lot. But only one of them earned money.

Morimoto: Yes, we also have a joint venture with AOL Time Warner. Actually though we don't pay great attention to movies directly, but to the content market as a whole. Because we own a joint venture, Toshiba-EMI, a music business that controls roughly 25% of the market here in Japan. So if we can put music together in product form with some other content, then we think there is a useful synergy.

But you have to look at our real goal here. Of course we are known as an electronic equipment maker, but we need some extra spice for our brand image – we want the customer to think of us in broader terms, as a brand name identified with having fun. The images of those kinds of content products are quite important to our place in society – they create more brand consciousness, they attract the attention of college-age young people, not only as customers but as potential employees. In that sense the content businesses have an important way of being helpful to us.

Author: So your aim is to build a sense of Toshiba culture in the market. You're not interested in purely investing to make movies in Hollywood?

Morimoto: I don't think so. We may join for some portion of a project if it fits us, but we don't plan to make a business of filmmaking investment.

Author: How about installing IT in the modern factory? Is it anything like the solutions business we just spoke of?

Morimoto: Yes it is. We can offer many, many types of industries the solutions for optimizing production with the IT skills we have learned and the technologies we make. You have to see each business from its own perspective. The maintenance business, for example, or the service type of business you find in power stations, or some other really legacy type of business, these are the things we call the old-economy industries and we don't think about them very much anymore. But Toshiba can supply the IT technology and know-how to revolutionize, or at least to put added value into, this kind of operation to create new profits for their owners and a new business for ourselves.

Author: This field called "data mining," sorting quickly through digital information about itself that Toshiba has collected, to find new ways to use the knowledge it already has – how does that work?

Morimoto: Well, data mining is quite important to us, and we've installed it as a new IT system in many of our businesses. Data mining is a lot like what it sounds like: thinking up different profiles and questions, so that we can use the information we already have on our customers to analyze their needs further and better than even *they* can, or to analyze what products are really attractive for the market. It should be a big earner for us.

Author: The Japanese government has coined a new buzzword, E-government systems. I suppose this means things like automatic teller machines at postal savings desks, e-mail information services from government offices to homes, and that sort of thing?

Morimoto: Yes, those areas of course have brought us some business opportunity – we do make things like automatic letter sorters, for example – but that is not so huge a business opportunity for the future. Because so many of our competitors can make the same things, [it's] just meeting government standards, and then applying for the contract and bidding it down to the point of no profit. Also, the government's fairness practices are to allocate procurement almost equally among the suppliers, so there's rarely a chance to build direct relations with the customers for more business.

Author: And what about Point-of-Sale technology, like computerized cash registers?

Morimoto: That's really handled by our subsidiary, Toshiba TEC, but it's a promising business. In Europe for example, the POS business and the personal computer business are docking: joining technologies through the medium of a server. So POS business customers aggressively support the PC business and the server business, as they learn what the combinations can do for them, so we have some synergy working there. These days, a POS machine by itself just doesn't stand for much. It should be connected, to extract the full value of the information. In Europe just like in Japan, for the past 20 years POS has been a very stand-alone business. But now that they [the technologies] are merging to communicate, expansion rates are promising.

Author: High-speed communications infrastructure: knowledge economy via the broadband, satellite, ground bases for digital transmission of TV, and things of this nature. Will these businesses make you a lot of money?

Morimoto: In Japan, yes.

Author: Elsewhere, it will be a national business in each country: national industries will be employed to build the infrastructure?

Morimoto: I think so. Because of the tie-in with existing national infrastructure.

Author: Transport Systems – car navigation aids, safety sensors, automatic toll-payment systems. Are they just for show, or real money-makers for the future?

Morimoto: That is a real question, to be honest. Some of them are working now. All the new systems will be demonstrated in the Nagoya area, where an Exposition is going to be put on. We are working with Toyota Motors on some things, and that is where maybe the first commercial application will be demonstrated, at the Expo. But we are most interested now in the automatic toll gate – because it's a real business now; there are electronic toll stations being built already on the expressway systems. The navigation and safety technologies, they take a little more time: a couple of years, or several years, I suppose.

Author: Medical Systems. Four per cent of Toshiba's income derives from your Medical Systems Company. Do you feel that's where it's going to stay?

Morimoto: Well, of course you could say medical systems again are a great deal like the media content business. Producing excellent medical systems gives us very much of a positive image before the public.

Author: But how are the profit margins in it?

Morimoto: To be honest the year FY 2000 was very bad. But in the past, the company's had a very steady profit, producing more than 10% operating income against sales, and so maybe next year it will come back.

Author: Why does it get bad so cyclically?

Morimoto: Well, business competition changed in 2000. And also we had some problems with the payout of the national medical insurance scheme, which meant many hospitals faced difficulties making money. But at the moment our competition is limited to GE, Siemens, and Philips, only four of us in the world doing this kind of thing.

Author: So all in all, you'll stay with it.

Morimoto: Yes.

Author: And, very important, what about home appliances?

Morimoto: This is kind of the origin of our business as a corporation, right? So maybe so many of the Japanese people have some nostalgia built up around this kind of business . . .

Author: The Carrier deal [a joint venture for global manufacture and sales of air conditioners between Toshiba and Carrier Corp.] was a good one, taking advantage of their global distribution: half the world is always in summer.

Morimoto: That's right, that is the reason why we made an alliance with Carrier. We are happy with that. But we really should be promoting it more, strengthening the business itself. The synergy impact within the Carrier and Toshiba venture is not big enough yet. But still, we're happy with it. By the same token, we may need to think more about ventures for home appliances. We have one now with Electrolux, but we have to push further on this question.

Author: Are you happy with the Electrolux joint venture results so far?

Morimoto: I think it's a good fit. We are strong in the Japan and Asian markets; they are strong in the US and Europe.

Author: So each of you can sell the synergies in your own markets?
Morimoto: Mmm. And then, perhaps, there is China: the battle-field in the future for household appliances.
Author: The securities analysts in town seem to be discouraged over Toshiba. As you know your stocks are quite low, and they seem to feel you aren't looking out sufficiently for share-holder value. And that a lot of businesses that are financially marginal should be gotten out of. Are you going to get out of them?
Morimoto: We are working on it. The first thing is, we have got to define our domains of what businesses to stay in, in what we think of as the industrial and individual and technological spheres, the core of our organization. Then we have to refine business models for each of the businesses we want to keep. As you know we have divided our business into ten in-house companies, our domains, already. Now the top corporate level should have initiative to take care of the overall Toshiba strategy itself, and also the brand strategy and the financial strategy. So we are going to strengthen those now, and use the Top-3 model as the basis of our plan to win with each product strategy in each competitive area.
Author: But this process has been going on for three years now.
Morimoto: More. Yes, of course.
Author: And the market has a right to ask, when do we begin to see the result in shareholder returns?
Morimoto: That's a difficult question for me. Of course we pay great attention to shareholder value itself. But this shareholder value, when we think about increasing it, we have to do that always in a time frame usually two or three years long. Not rushing to immediately increase it. Every quarter some enterprise will disclose the quarter's results. But in a Japanese company quarter-based *management* itself causes difficulties, brings us prob-lems. Because Japanese management has always looked with a

little bit longer view, a little further into the future, to create shareholder values. And to throw away that process now would be to throw away our very foundations.

CHAPTER TWENTY-FIVE
MANAGING FOR TIGHT TIMES

In its business years ending in March 1999 and March 2000, Toshiba reported its first net losses in 23 years: a combined 42 billion yen, for both years. While the situation reversed to a 96.1 billion yen net profit for the year ending in March 2001, and the train seemed to be energetically back on track with the largest profit since 1991, the interlude of red ink had been rattlingly embarrassing to Toshiba's top management. The oldest-line, biggest Japanese corporations, dealing in the highest technology and fastest-growing industries, are not supposed to finish in the red, period.

For the year ending in March 2002, however, Toshiba was estimating in late 2001 not only that it would book more losses, but 200 billion yen (over a billion and a half dollars) worth of them for the single year alone.

In 2000, Toshiba's stock price had risen on the Tokyo Exchange as high as 1,280 yen per share. In mid 2001, it was vacillating between the 400s and the 500s.

Credit ratings on Toshiba bonds had been falling through the calendar year 2001; while major Japanese competitors carried market capitalization values roughly equal to half their annual revenues in the Forbes International 500 Listings published in July 2001, only Toshiba and Mitsubishi Electric had market worths of just a third their total annual revenues.[1]

A corporate raider, if hostile takeovers were to be permitted in Japan's M&A markets, would require only just over six billion dollars to command 51% of Toshiba, at a stock price of 450 yen. And practical control of the company might be had with a lot fewer shares than that.

In early November 2001, business conditions for most of the electrical/electronics giants of Japan were becoming so abysmal that an executive of the larger Matsushita Electric Industrial, makers of both Panasonic and National brands and the eighteenth largest non-American corporation in the world, warned that even his own company could be "an easy target for a takeover" if performance did not improve by the end of the next fiscal year.[2]

"Actually," admitted Toshiba's Chief Financial Officer, Senior Executive Vice President Kiyoaki Shimagami in an interview in July 2001, "I was just secretly studying the ways to defend ourselves [from a takeover]."

Shimagami reckons that about 30% of his shareholders are "stable," a term relevant to the Japanese practices of cross-shareholding that grew out of the old *keiretsu* financial and main-bank groups, as well as to certain investors, such as insurance companies or employee stockholding groups, expected to remain loyal. It would be a good fight, he thinks.

"But of course, when or if it comes, there should be other tactical ways to defend ourselves." One of them, he reckons carefully, is to try to reduce fixed costs by changing into an "asset-light" corporate structure. In other words, by divestiture, which is mainly the shedding of affiliated companies and businesses that Chairman Nishimuro and President Okamura are working on and have been for years.

Neither of those two executives was willing, of course, to speak bluntly about what properties are likely to go on the block – although the Chairman hinted, as an example of what can be done, that Toshiba might be willing to part with some or all of its controlling 37% stake in Toshiba Tungaloy, a super-hard-tool-making subsidiary with a market value of almost 22 billion yen as of early November 2001.[3]

Whether assets are fixed or liquid, they can still attract takeover attempts if the price is temptingly low. Toshiba's assets had a book value in April 2001 of 50 billion dollars, and a debt level of just under 15 billion dollars. While all its issued stock, in the 450 yen per share range, had a value of around 13 billion dollars.

No one could say whether Toshiba would try to find a "white knight" or concoct a "poison pill" to try to fight off anyone unwelcome. No one knows if it could. At the level of Toshiba such battles – on this scale – have never been fought in Japan.

But Toshiba has known managerial and market crisis before, and the plans it intends relying upon are much more those of internal management strategies than financial maneuvering. "We must understand that we are encountering a huge risk," said a corporate statement in November 2001, as S&P placed Toshiba on negative credit watch. "[President] Okamura strongly urged all Toshiba employees to implement the 01 Action Plan and accelerate all restructuring programs in order to overcome the current difficulties."

It was, of course, the immediacy of those difficulties – mostly, the gut-wrenchingly disastrous years of global IT business downturn, starting in 2000 – that composed the risk. By the end of 2001 it was becoming more and more likely that the looked-for recovery of global economies and industries was still far off. Both America and Japan were sinking in recession at the time, and most analysts were shaking their heads at predictions for true recovery in the IT fields any earlier than 2003.

In Toshiba's annual report of March 2001, Nishimuro and Okamura wrote to investors that "90% of (all Toshiba's) sales growth in fiscal 2003 is expected to derive from IT-related businesses." By November, not eight months later, the plans were changing drastically.

"Personally, I think half of our colleagues are accepting the situation, in other words positively. Because we have to change. But half of my colleagues maybe do not understand what is happening around us . . . they don't understand the real meaning in the change in the business environment. But as you know, Toshiba's competency is in its people. We have so many talented people. So I believe we can survive in the future in this business situation."

Assessment of the immediate impact of management change on Toshiba, given by a ranking operations executive

Chairman Nishimuro smiles when the question of acquisition by an outsider is raised. "If we raised the charm of Toshiba to the level where somebody wanted to acquire us – that's actually something we should do. We wouldn't sell, but we'd be happy to be asked: it would be nice to know we look so good that somebody wants to buy us!"

Beyond jokes, however, the management team on the executive floor is looking seriously at the tasks ahead. The plans that have been laid are manifold, and most of them, to an outsider, seem sound if not very ground-breaking. One is to require Toshiba's top 100 executives to regularly add to a personal portfolio of the company's stock – the closest Nishimuro feels he can come under the Japanese administrative system to a stock-option incentive.

More crucial are an acceleration of the steps under way to sell off unprofitable or just plain unnecessary businesses. First up was a goal to achieve as quickly as possible the liquidation of three-and-three-quarters billion dollars' worth of operating assets. "The negotiations are already underway, it's true. [But] if you start with that exact target, you may not actualize an end figure of 450 billion yen [due to failure of some negotiations]. So actually we have 600 billion yen as candidate assets right now, to make sure we hit our target." (450 billion yen equals about 7% of Toshiba's book value, not counting its debt.)

President Okamura has drastic expediencies on his mind too. "I think we're better off preparing for the worst-case scenario, whereby the recovery does not come within a year from now. Nobody can forecast what will happen [in the economy] . . . but in the short run the Japanese economy cannot be foreseen to recover.

"I have just announced in my investor relations meetings overseas that we must accelerate all the measures of Toshiba's mid-term plan [which was unveiled only in April 2001], and execute them more quickly. Intensified competitiveness will be enhanced.

"The mid-term plan had a goal line of the year 2003. But we want to implement it all much faster now, so that by the end of summer [2001] we'll be able to set new targets. In essence it will be a faster implementation of the same plan."

The blueprint used for achieving all these mid-term plan goals (discussed briefly below) is what Toshiba calls the 01 Action Plan: a sort of executive-summary guide to achieving the much-contracted schedules of the mid-term plan. "It has three major strategies. The first is for the new in-house companies to form their own definition of how they should conduct business, change their management systems. On that I think we were able to come up with a certain shape of new management already. However I can't, unfortunately, say that this change was so fundamental that it's correlated to actual performance or result.

"For example, we need to get out of the stereotyped traditional social infrastructure type business [model] and into something with much more of an advanced business model. We can use high technology like computers and semiconductors to refine these water and electricity systems, and we can sell them globally instead of just at home.

"The second strategy has been to review totally our industrial portfolio. This still needs work as well: with the exception of three in-house companies, I don't think there's been much fundamental change in the structure of the business we do. They are making alliances and ventures of their own, inside and outside Japan, but these were still limited to consolidation of our peripheral businesses.

"And third was the challenge to change our corporate culture, through adaptation of Six Sigma job methodology. Here again, I think we can already see some effects of it, but for the time being the effects are still superficial."

Perhaps Okamura will enjoy a little more sharply focused attention when he urges more achievement from his executive team under the 01 Action Plan. Part of it, the Toshiba adaptation of an "economic value added" strategy called by the company the "Toshiba Value Created" system of performance metrics, effects a new salary scheme for supervisors at the general manager or higher level. From now on, says Senior Executive Vice President and Strategic Planning Chief Yasuo Morimoto, remuneration at these levels will be decided 80% on business results.

While both Chairman Nishimuro and President Okamura are careful to explain their own management philosophies as a mixture of the old-style consensus formulation, with the new-style executive goal-setting and method-selection, it's also true they know parts of the giant organization are not responding to what they ask quickly enough.

But with 80% of their pay now based on performance (the difference between highest and lowest pay after adjustment for performance will come to an eight million yen variance), the mid- and upper-level management should at the least all be reacting very positively when the president seeks their consensus.

A less happy expediency that Toshiba has forced on itself through embrace of the 01 Action Plan is something that few in the executive ranks actively wanted to see: Toshiba decided to reduce its work force. A net of twenty thousand employees –

more than 10% of the worldwide work force[4] – were to leave the company before the close of the fiscal year in March 2002. Most of the reduction will come through natural attrition or voluntary early retirement plans, but not all. Thousands will indeed be forced to leave, which is a hard thing for any Toshiba worker, at any level, to face.

For a company like Toshiba, who long stood on the principle of Japanese and corporate culture against the advice of business and securities analysts and many of the 25% of its shareholders who are foreigners, to cut payroll as the routine and fast way to lower fixed expenses, it was a humbling experience.

NOTES

1. "The World Super 50," *Forbes Magazine*, global edition, 23 July 2001
2. "Matsushita Executive Warns of Takeover," *Wall Street Journal*, 2 November 2001
3. "Tokyo Stock Exchange Weekly Closing," *Nikkei Weekly*, 5 November 2001
4. "Toshiba to slash 20,000 jobs," *Asahi Shimbun*, 27 August 2001

CHAPTER TWENTY-SIX
STRATEGIC PLANNING:
THE CRUCIBLE

While Japan taught the world so many things about quality, about consensus management, about involving everybody, one of the things Japan has had trouble doing is being rigorous about pruning weak businesses, and letting them merge with other businesses to become strong.

> Jack Welch,
> retired chairman, General Electric
> Quoted in Reuters News Service, 8 November 2001

They [Toshiba] can't suddenly discover a business that no one else is doing and try to build a niche there, which is what Canon did 20 years ago with laser printers.

> Richard Kaye,
> securities analyst, Merrill Lynch
> Quoted in Reuters News Service, 8 November 2001

There it is, then: the question for Toshiba. How far must it go in stripping away businesses that it decides are truly non-essential?

Welch's remarks were not directed at Toshiba, but the point he raised, and the correlate observed beneath it about the nature of new businesses in the IT age, are ones that Chairman Nishimuro, President Okamura, and all of the top Toshiba executives, who have sliced deeply already at Toshiba's losing operations, must go on measuring until some correct answer is arrived at. But how will they know it when they see it?

Does every single one of the Toshiba businesses retained have to place in the Top Three rankings in the world? In an enterprise betting on markets as yet unrealized, can it be solely a question of profit and loss?

Bailing out of a business like DRAMs cuts the uncertainty of the product's notorious cyclicality – but it also writes off enormous sunk costs. Preparing for the "next wave" of high-margin technology products seems to be something Toshiba is good at. But how can you know you've got the future equivalent of a market-devouring laser printer among your competencies, unless you sink a nosebleed-fortune into constant research & development to keep pace in literally dozens of technologies from which such a product might spring?

How do you know where the line is between cutting enough, and cutting too many, of the employees who can quickly bring that product to market?

There are strategic models for softening the spikes on these questions, and we can see them at work in a brief review of Toshiba's formal strategic planning frameworks.

After the reform of the corporate structure which created ten in-house companies, all with the independence to pursue their core businesses on their own plan lines, Toshiba laid down some essential guidelines in its Mid-Term Business Plan in the spring of 2001.

- The first part of the plan was an instruction for the new companies to aim to increase corporate value – to grow – not only by acting in isolation, but by employing the skills and technologies of sister companies. The results would be measured concretely, all Toshiba people were told, by use of the new metric, Toshiba Value Created (TVC), which would measure capital returns against the cost of capital.

- The second part was that Toshiba would re-acculturate itself and its management plans by moving as close as it possibly could to the market. The Voice of the Customer was the axis of this tactic, and summed up, it realized the importance of speed-to-market by acknowledging that Toshiba had to listen to exactly what people wanted to buy before making it.

• The third commandment was that Toshiba would focus its resources on Information Technology, announcing a plan for 1.2 trillion yen worth of research & development outlays over the next three years – with 70% of it aimed at IT fields.

• The fourth directive was to strengthen the profits earned by the "legacy" businesses of Toshiba, that is the non-IT areas such as heavy electrical machinery, infrastructure systems like water and power grids, and home appliances.

The goals of the mid-term plan were to achieve a net income of 200 billion yen, which would be Toshiba's largest ever and would furnish return on equity to shareholders of 14.4%, with a large reduction of total debt, by March 2004. The goals for the first year of the Plan could not be met. It is highly questionable whether the goals for the next year will be, either.

In light of the damaging blows that the continuing weakness of the domestic economy (62% of Toshiba's business is in the home market) and the stagnation in so many of the world IT industries have delivered, it was perhaps understandable that President Okamura told a *Nikkei Sangyo* reporter on 10 July 2001 that "I think Toshiba has focused too much on IT business, and has not revealed enough our efforts to enhance business in stable areas. What we need to pursue is the two-way direction of stabilizing profit in growing industries and enhancing our position in existing markets."[1]

At the same time Toshiba sought to spark a revolution in the thinking of workers and managers in general, everywhere inside the company. The Management Innovation 2001 plan, which set out the goal of regularly achieving 10% return on equity for Toshiba shareholders, was designed to sharpen all business activities with "agile management" and innovation on the job, by reforming the work flows into units of dedicated, specialist groups.

What all this meant, the MI 2001 plan, was that Toshiba was going on the Six Sigma standard. The theoretical methodology is complex, but the *New York Times* summarized it in an article in mid 2001 as "a quality control method for increasing efficiency and reducing errors [in any job] to 3.5 defects per million operations, [which] draws on the same customer-focused, analytical methods of its predecessor [Total Quality Management]."[2]

Other companies have adopted Six Sigma, including Sony and GE, and the main principle is that to work well, the plan must be installed organization-wide.

It's a big challenge. The key is thrusting upon every employee the responsibility for identifying problems, bringing them to work-group attention, and then either leading or joining in an effort to analyze the cause, correct it, and make sure it doesn't recur. Everyone must take a turn as a Six Sigma project leader; every business line in Toshiba is under instructions to "benchmark" its products and improvement results against the acknowledge best of all its competitors. Combined with the TVC principle, it also micro-measures costs, and ranks each employee's performance by the success of his or her participation. Ideally, it will make each Toshiba man and woman aware of the direct financial results of his or her own and everyone else's job performance.

There are some potential complications to applying Six Sigma everywhere in a company like Toshiba: how do you rate the cost-of-capital return performance on an R&D engineer who spends months patiently researching a new technology that may not find an application for years? And its reliance on top-down, super-refined control of every aspect of the job may leave little room for bottom-up creative input on the work floor.

President Okamura himself scored the job of embedding Six Sigma at Toshiba only 40% complete at the time of the *Nikkei Sangyo* interview.[3] But, this is a strategy for the decades ahead and not just the lean days of the early 2000s. Successful completion could well be a factor in how intelligently Toshiba answers the question at the top of this chapter. The company has assigned a corporate vice president, Toshio Yonezawa, of the Management Innovation Division to oversee the installation of Six Sigma, and if enthusiasm could do the job his would push success to the 100% stage by next Friday.

Six Sigma is not all there is to Management Innovation 2001, however. The third of eight steps toward achieving MI 2001 goals, according to one academic template Toshiba is using, is "clear vision to lead direction and motivate action."

And as the profit and loss shadows grew long, symbolically and literally, around Toshiba in the fading half of the year 2001, it was the investors who were championing "action."

The 01 Action Plan was Toshiba's response. As President Okamura explained to an audience of investors in July, it was drawn up as a solution to the declining business environment. "What we really need to do," as he saw it, "is to accelerate business strategies based on [the mid-term plan].

"The vehicle is our 01 Action Plan, initiated in mid June," aimed at, among other things, "the speedy achievement of asset reduction and streamlined management. I have told our headquarters staff and in-house companies to complete short lists of priority projects as quickly as possible, with a deadline of the end of this month . . . I will review [these . . . and] assure the immediate execution of the selected projects."

"In May, all the [in-house] company presidents had some kind of sense for crisis," President Okamura had told a reporter.[4] And here the crisis was.

In late August 2001, Toshiba delivered its Action Plan to an apprehensive global family of employees. The sad list of the reasons for its "execution" came first:

- In the personal-computer market there was low demand, and fierce price competition reigned in both America and Europe.
- Semiconductors were reporting more than 30% losses in demand.
- Liquid Crystal Devices were suffering a big supply–demand gap.
- Mobile Phones had tripped over delayed service starts in the next-generation product.
- Japan itself was undergoing both recession and deflation.

Under the broad headings of "Intensifying competitiveness" and "Streamlining management," Toshiba's chiefs proposed, among other things:

- To create new business models. An integrator model would lead to an even more open business structure, relying more on outside suppliers and partners and less on Toshiba in-house production. A market-defining model would continue to aim for the very top, with spectacular, trend-setting Toshiba-branded products that would make their own new markets and bring in high margins. A platform model would supply Toshiba designs, patents, assembly and product technologies on an "open market" to other firms, perhaps to competitors. (If these plans sound a lot like what Toshiba was already doing, they are – but on a much-advanced scale.)
- To reduce corporate debts by 450 billion yen by March 2004, with 150 billion coming from divestiture of unprofitable businesses and reorganization of affiliates, and 300 billion from financial securitization strategies, such as the packaging and marketing of instruments based on Toshiba's receivables.

- To reduce procurement costs by 150 billion yen, 20%, over the next two years through standardizing and joint-venture buying operations.
- To reduce worldwide employment by 20,000, with the greater part, 17,000, being subtracted through attrition, voluntary early retirement, or separation in Japan itself.
- To liquidate within the 2003 fiscal year 800 billion yen worth of assets.

By now of course the answer to the question at the top of this chapter is plain. Toshiba is intensifying the strategies of a conglomerate. It knows very well that it is too big, and would like – under the merciless prod of a very lean business period – to get smaller faster.

But every part, every player has to be considered carefully, and both has been and will be by executives at the strategy helm. In a sense, everything about Toshiba – a 54-billion-dollar-a-year company that's never run a net profit higher than 130 billion yen (a little more than a billion dollars, or only about 2% of its most recent gross income, at late-2001 exchange rates) – is a sunk cost.

And in this age, who can guarantee what the next laser-printer market phenomenon will turn out to be? The Merrill Lynch man was right – Toshiba can't now make that kind of choice. The quarter or third or half of itself that Toshiba might divest, to focus on returning big profits by aiming its fixed costs and further R&D outlays at a handful of promising technologies, might indeed turn out to be the pieces that would have provided those technologies. Who could have foreseen that the slow-moving colossus, known for generators and locomotives and refrigerators, would grow rich and make it to No. 2 in the world with its DRAMs? Or that the same DRAMs might someday wound it so badly?

Toshiba, for better or for worse, will always be Big. It plans to speed ahead; it still might, in some or many areas, fall behind.

Its strategic plans might be excellent; they might be unrealistic. It's a big job, as we've seen, just setting up a meaningful system to *measure* its success or failure. But whatever the immediate results of all its plans, Toshiba will always be a work in progress.

NOTES

1. "Okamura's Innovation Just Started," *Nikkei Sangyo Shimbun*, 10 July 2001
2. "Quality Revival, Part 2: Ford Embraces Six Sigma," *New York Times*, 13 June 2001
3. "Okamura's Innovation Just Started."
4. "Okamura's Innovation Just Started."

CHAPTER TWENTY-SEVEN
THE CHINA CARD

Meet Nobumasa Hirata, a man who hasn't had a day off in two months. He's been too busy building Toshiba's newest major market.

"Racing to build" might be a better choice of words. Toshiba's business in China has been more than a mirror image of the international IT slowdown that was plaguing the company for more than a year in late 2001: it was a bonanza.

Hirata, Chairman of the Board of Toshiba (China) Co., Ltd., ticks off the figures. There's an expected two billion dollars in sales from FY 2001 (ending in March 2002), plus a billion dollars more in sales from Toshiba subsidiaries in Hong Kong that serve the Chinese market. That three-billion-dollar total would come to more than 6.5% of the entire net sales of all of Toshiba Corp. worldwide – from a subsidiary only six years old!

And the still-better news is that 60% of that gross figure was expected to originate from sales made *in* the Chinese market. Sales of Toshiba goods made in China, and sold to the Chinese, in fact, were expected to expand at a rate of 50% in the single year 2001–2002. Far from using China as a mere cheap-labor manufacturing base, Toshiba is becoming as embedded a player in the Chinese economy as it is in the American.

The company has invested more than three-quarters of a billion dollars in China so far, owns 22 subsidiaries and five representative offices there, and employs 10,000 Chinese. "Most of the major activity divisions of Toshiba," says Hirata, "are already present in China." In fact Dalian Toshiba Television Co., Ltd., in northern China, produces all television sets for the Japanese market (including the new digital models), as well as all of Toshiba's output for its 2% of the Chinese market.

He notes that Toshiba China is already in negotiations with Chinese firms to set up a joint venture on the continent to turn out electric-railway rolling stock, and also toward a separate joint venture to make and supply digital television broadcasting equipment of almost every description. "Digital broadcasting is already present in Japan," Hirata notes, "and we can foresee that within a few years it will also start up in China."

And, there is already a venture set up to manufacture mobile-phone handsets in Beijing's choice of CDMA technology, called TD-SCDMA. The cell-phone market in China is mammoth, with an estimated 120 million numbers in use by mid 2001[1] and possibly 150,000 phones sold every day, according to one eye-popping account in the Japanese business press.[2]

While in general labor costs in China are a tenth of what they are in Japan, and overall expenses including transportation and logistics, Hirata estimates, are from 15 to 30% smaller than what they would be for making similar products in Japan, all foreign-capital competitors enjoy about the same advantages – and the purely Chinese competitors can still beat Japan makers' prices by 50%.

It is, he means to say, an entirely new competitive structure, gateway to what is looming as an entirely new and vast market-place. Pointing to at least one major Chinese manufacturer that even does its own R&D on products like televisions and large home appliances, Hirata says "this remarkable learning curve that the Chinese local manufacturers have shown in the past one or two years has been so intense that only those of us who are based locally can really grasp it."

And his own blunt deduction is: "In a way one could say that it is now a result that Japanese companies that have *not* established manufacturing bases in China cannot survive."

The growth figures, whether in manufacturing or in bottom-line income, may be expanding now so rapidly as to startle Japan. But they won't always grow at 50% a year, for Toshiba or anyone else, Hirata knows. That is why he is taking the longest-possible strategic view of China as a market, which means a perception of China as a nation and as an amalgam of cultures, where Toshiba needs to be accepted both as a brand and as a permanent member in good standing of the national business community (Toshiba already uses some 1,000 local Chinese suppliers for its parts procurement).

That is also why he was not getting many days off in 2001. "My first major mission when I went to China was to enhance Toshiba's image. So, over the first year, I took part in more than 50 interviews and press conferences, meeting over a thousand media representatives in total." Hirata became so well known that he was on the invitee lists of internationally themed conferences all over China: Beijing, Shanghai, Xian, etc. "They're almost always held on weekends, but what else could I do?

"It's necessary," he says of his personal participation. "Whoever deals with China, coming from our country, first has this burden of the interpretation of the [Great Pacific] War between our two countries, and that means one has to deal with the sentiments of the Chinese people."

Japan's invasion of China and the sufferings the Imperial Army troops inflicted on the populace are still a recollection reiterated periodically by the Beijing government, much the way Russians remember the German invasion of World War II. It is an area of public dialogue where any representative of Japan must tread very lightly.

"So I thought the way to alleviate this problem was to meet with as many young intellectual people, or as many media people, as I could to explain why Toshiba is here, who I am, what we are trying to do in China. I really think I may be the first Japanese businessman ever to do so. Since then our two top executives, the chairman and the president, have made a special effort to respond in the same way. Chairman Nishimuro is on record as recognizing that a global company active in China must send out messages to the Chinese people not through advertising, but through public relations and direct contact. I think the two of them are the most covered foreign businessmen in the Chinese media since Jack Welch and Bill Gates."

With an eye to the longer-range involvement of Toshiba in China, the company in the spring of 2001 opened its fourth corporate R&D center in Beijing. As Sumio Kuniyoshi, Senior Manager of the China Department, International Div., summarizes it, "One reason for having an R&D base there is the excellent human resources to be found in China; another is to develop Chinese voice-synthesis and voice-recognition technology, and that can only be done in China."

Toshiba has in fact focused so tightly on its future in China that it has recently added a director who is a former Japanese ambassador to that country. A former president and chairman of Toshiba, Toshio Doko, has also served as chairman of the Japan-China Economic Association. Following this tradition, former president of Toshiba Sugiichiro Watari is now serving as the current chairman of this association.

Hirata says Toshiba has been scrupulously careful, throughout its 30-year history of dealings with China, not to become involved in any way with the notorious corruption problems that the country is now trying to clean up after its accession to the World Trade Organization. There have been some problems, with counterfeiting of Toshiba goods and accountability in the distribution chain. "We just have to be sure to choose trustworthy companies to handle our distribution, and make sure we sell only to resellers that we are sure will pay us the full proceeds."

China is no "gold rush" to uninitiates. Foreign business people from all industries must carefully learn the ground there before committing resources. But Toshiba feels good about its own future, especially in having moved so close to the "Voice of the Customer" with such a full range of products. It's betting that the "China card," well-played, is bound to turn into a full deck of opportunities – and Toshiba needs them very much.

Toshiba's Subsidiaries, Affiliates, and Alliances in China

Northern Region
Shengyang Toshiba Elevator Co.
Toshiba Dalian Co.
Henan Pinggao Toshiba High-Voltage Switchgear Co.
Shengyang NETS System Integration Co.
Dalian Toshiba Television Co.

Central Coastal Region
Jiangsu Honshiba Tontru Network System Equipment Co.
Nanjing Postal Wong Zhi Telecommunications Co.
Changzhou Toshiba Transformer Co.
Shanghai Xinzhi Electronics Co.
Toshiba Technology Development (Shanghai) Co.
Toshiba Computer Systems (Shanghai) Co.
Hangzhi Machinery & Electronics Co.
Wuxi Huazhi Semiconductor Co.
Shanghai Toshiba Elevator Co.
Ningbo Toshiba Huatong Switchgear Co.

Southern Coastal Region
Tsurong Xiamen Xiangyu Trading Co.
Guangdong Meizhi Compressor Co.

Toshiba Copying Machine (Shenzhen) Co.
Zhuhai Xujizhi Power System Automation Co.
Jiangxi Toshiba Electronic Materials Co.
Guangdong Meizhi Compressor Motor Co.

NOTES

1. "Investors Fear China's Mobile-Phone Market Is Saturated," *Wall Street Journal*, 23 August 2001
2. "Rush is on to build huge IT market," *Nikkei Weekly*, 6 August 2001

CHAPTER TWENTY-EIGHT
THE IMAGINATIVE LEAP

Once a company has slipped down the competitive slope . . . its rivals will already have moved ahead, and it may fail to break into new technology, products and markets altogether. To get out of this trap it must make an imaginative leap and face up to the reality of global competition.

Toshiba's New British Company:
Competitiveness Through Innovation in Industry
Malcolm Trevor
(Policy Studies Institute, London, 1988)

Some final observations from the notes of a fascinated observer:

Neither for sentiment nor the habituations of industrial empire has Toshiba decided to stay diversified, and to pour as much capital into maintaining its competencies as business realities will allow.

In the first chapter, it was remarked "how the continuation of fierce competitions among these old rivals . . . in Japan as well as abroad, has added a strategic dimension of external support to the precarious risk structures these behemoths now carry."

In brief, that support is:

- A community of like manufacturers making like products across a like spectrum, who cannot afford any more than Toshiba to "go it alone" in expensive, independent technology developments to support every product line in the repertoire. All these enterprises – dozens of them – are of business necessity not only Toshiba's competitors but its customers, just as Toshiba is customer to them. Hundreds, thousands of components amounting to billions of dollars in total trade change hands among them annually. It's an invisible market, a profit structure of enormous proportions that the customer never sees any more than he or she ever really sees the "Intel Inside."

- At the highest level, these largest of competitors can parlay their skills into technological alliances not just to buy and sell components, but to invent, develop, and manufacture them together. The capital risks of overhead, of development, of betting on a dangerously long-term strategy are cut in half, by two-thirds, by three-quarters, depending on how capitalization of an alliance is split between the new "partners." If the target customer is, say, the young consumer, a partnership with a Sony, which enjoys a gold-standard reputation with those consumers and a very strong distribution and marketing structure to reach them, can maximize sales reach by handling the finished product under its name alone, as with PlayStation 2 and its "Toshiba aboard." Toshiba concluded some 22 of these strategic alliances in the year 2000 alone.

- These alliances, financing the truly big bets of the IT world, are feasible for Toshiba *only* if it maintains world-leading products and technologies. And with today's worldwide speed-to-market capabilities almost the ultimate arbiter of who will be the winner – namely the combination and economy of technology with design-development, and with quick, reliable manufacture – is part of the package of competency the allies all want.

- The "commodities" business that Toshiba so abhors on account mainly of its low margins is really one of the businesses it is in, in precisely the form of component sales. Toshiba does not have to knock down the prices or resort to discount sales venues for its own top-quality branded goods such as DVD movie players because it can make the equivalent of discount-sale profits *in* the components market, where only its client corporation knows its brand.

- As an integrator – the role this strategy and its tactics impose upon Toshiba as surely as owning factories makes it a manufacturer – the company can use the same strategies in *its* networks of smaller external suppliers, such as the 400 who furnish more than 75% of everything that goes into the Toshiba portable computer assembled at Ome. It designs the component to the most economic and efficient specifications its great engineering genius can achieve, and then asks its family of competent suppliers to bid on the job, with quality and just-in-time manufacturing specifications written in to match Ome's practices perfectly.

CAN THEY MANAGE IT?

Far below the majestic, sweeping views from the executive floor of Toshiba's Tokyo headquarters lies an organization of 188,000 – as complex in activity, intent, and passion as any medium-size city, excepting that the sun never sets on it. Or on the cultural diversities all its crafts and geographic dimensions imply.

Beneath the broad restructuring umbrella first opened by then-President Nishimuro, there are plans upon plans for managing all this, some made in good times for bad and others made in bad times for good. It's hard for an outsider to judge their efficacy, in combination.

But one thing to keep an observer's eye on in Toshiba going forward is, how well does all the master planning answer the biggest challenge the chairman and the president face: to change Toshiba from an engineering culture to a marketing culture, without disenfranchising any of the enormous support structures Toshiba currently has?

Think of Toshiba's management ideal as horizontal scale lines, each representing an in-house company, crossed by vertical scale lines, each representing a technological competence. The need here falls upon the intersections: to spread the wealth of technical and manufacturing capabilities of Toshiba, all across the many markets of Toshiba.

Social Infrastructure Systems Co., that is, needs to know how digital control systems can be applied to make a water-purification system more efficient, less costly, and more exactly what the customer needs. e-Solutions Co. needs to gain enough trust of its customers to hear their real problems, not their internal excuses, so that a new IT system can be assembled and installed that actually solves them.

In putting men and women to work inside these new matrices, the last thing Toshiba's leaders want to do is make them afraid they are being displaced – or to tempt them to displace each other. The Golden Rule is that all of the 188,000 workers within this matrix, most of them utter strangers to each other, must be able to trust their own career goals to other Toshiba people anywhere else within it, to be able to join effectively in putting together winning products. Aside from the huge work needed to install the matrix and get it to work (in the midst of horrendous economic challenges), Toshiba's leaders must stand guarantee that this will be the precise function of the new Corporation.

It isn't, of course, easy for a chief executive to make this kind of promise ring true in uncertain times. Quite likely it's in part for such reasons that, when Nishimuro reduced his board of directors from 34 to 13, instead of bringing in younger men, or women, or foreigners, for fresher input, he chose simply to keep the 13 most senior of the old board members. The seniority system is not displaced.

So far the enterprise seems in good hands. "He is a very, very impressive, perhaps unique individual," is how Chairman Nishimuro is characterized by Stanford Research Institute head Samuel Armacost, who visits Toshiba executives twice a year in his role as member of the company's International Advisory Committee – and who has himself sat on many corporate boards. "He has the ability to think in global competitive context, but operate within the culture of what is still a big Japanese company. He's done some very brave things there."

"Unique"? That's the problem. When he leaves the management scene, and then President Okamura follows, where can Toshiba find their like as leaders?

COMPETENCIES AND LIABILITIES

The spectrum of Toshiba's superior technological capabilities is obviously amazing. It is also a little worrisome. First, even though Toshiba tried to recoup its R&D outlays by moving the design process as close to the manufacturing level as possible, and even though it tries to share risk by forming developmental alliances with other top-flight competitors, high-technology development, taken by itself, from here on will continue to be a cash-flow corporate nosebleed. With lead-cycles of ten to five years in the preliminary research stages, the company's competencies are going to be enormously costly tools, and are going to grow more costly even while the certainty of their returns lessens.

Not only because some technologies might fail, ending up as total write-offs rather than keys to high-margin sales. But also because of, as Armacost puts it, the "collapsing utility curve. You can drive technology in terms of form and function . . . so quickly you can get to the stage where consumers won't pay for it on the same cycle [that they used to].

"People used to buy [for example] portable PCs every six or eight or nine months at the early edge of the adopter phase just because that was the next increment of capacity. Those issues are being driven by technology, and by price . . . [and] people say, 'Gee, I'm not using the function I've got. You could drop the price and double the function, and [still] I don't need it yet . . .'

"I think the utility curves are changing so quickly relative to the value curve that used to exist that you have to be much more careful every day about how much you spend in terms of how quickly you need to get it back, because you may not have enough time in the marketplace with a particular technology to get your returns out."

The *sine qua non* of competition, speed-to-market, curtails the product cycle.

And secondly, even if you are careful, the very nature of technology-based competition tends to produce a trend that lowers returns quickly. The starting point of Six Sigma organization-wide product improvement, as Toshiba interprets it, is to select "benchmarks" – the best model produced by any competitor in the market – and try to equal or surpass them. When all or most companies follow that pattern, of marketing high-technology wrapped in high-quality, "It results in competitive convergence, which means that all the competitors in an industry imitate each other in a zero-sum competition that erodes price and destroys profitability."[1] In other words, the products become more and more indistinguishably excellent.

Another compulsion for tearing Toshiba away from the engineering culture, and toward the marketing culture: to shift the competitive grounds from production-driven to value-added, so the customer is offered a Toshiba product that holds meaning for himself – not necessarily for Toshiba.

ANALYSIS

We have to live today by what truth we can get today and be ready tomorrow to call it falsehood.

William James

Toshiba's tale does not quicken the hearts of stock market analysts. Pointing out that his own firm was maintaining its neutral rating on Toshiba, Takatoshi Yamamoto, vice-chairman and managing director of Morgan Stanley Dean Witter, said in June 2001 that "if we just discuss some comparison among the five major (similarly) competitive companies – Toshiba, Hitachi, Mitsubishi (Electric), Fujitsu, and NEC – Toshiba might be the most struggling company." Aware that, in Yamamoto's words, "Toshiba has great strengths in devices and especially in the portable PC business . . . over the three- to five-year time frame ahead, how can we expect continuing stable profits from the PC business alone, or from the semiconductor business itself? [You can make such forecasts] only if you recognize them as a [value-added] systematized or total solution [product].

"However in terms of common sense it's pretty difficult to discuss the PC, or purely semiconductors, as secular growth devices or equipment over five years. We can't say."

He can't say, and he isn't about to raise the neutral recommendation any higher as long as Toshiba can come up with no scenario – even its restructuring – that "takes care of investors' interests" better over the mid- to long-term. As he sees it, Toshiba's plan to build growth by drawing closer to customers sounds all too much like what competitors Hitachi and

Mitsubishi Electric are pledging to do, too. "All three are the same type of companies – is it valuable for [Toshiba] to do business like [two other] companies? . . . These three should continue kind of more independent businesses . . . even if losing money."

Ah, there's the rub. If Toshiba shouldn't mind losing money to experiment with doing business "differently," why should investors mind losing money along with them?

To be fair to both sides, this opinion was aired in mid 2001, when there was still faint optimism in the air for economic rebound in America, or somewhere, by the last half, or the last quarter, of that year. When there still seemed a chance that Toshiba's stock prices would rebound on an economic upturn, or the corporation could still show results that would make them rebound.

That hadn't happened as of late 2001. And securities companies are, after all, in the business of finding profit opportunities in stocks for their own customers and shareholders. One might forgive their reluctance to endorse Toshiba's enthusiasm, pledges of serious reorganizational effort notwithstanding.

Toshiba's cash flow might be enough to withstand recessionary pressures on capital supply from the market for a while. But other analysts point out where it does hurt: acquisitions, mergers that Toshiba might effect to great advantage in acquiring even market share, let alone competence or intellectual property, either in Japan or overseas, are being excluded because of the fear of impact on share price. Acquired companies are usually bought, at least in part, with shares of the purchaser's stock, and at their low values Toshiba would need to transfer a lot of them to make a purchase, even on 2001's highly devalued technological assets. There's no guarantee the purchase wouldn't dilute the share values still further, really crippling the buyer.

Of course Toshiba may have no desires to invest in anything

more than the present developmental alliances anyway. But the pressures of Economy 2001 also hit Toshiba and its competitors hard in another sector: it forced the whole field of Japanese electronic/electrical manufacturers to cut their payrolls, through attrition, buyouts, or layoffs, by something over 100,000 employees. It's an action that Nishimuro and Okamura, for the reasons explained above, fought hard not to take at Toshiba.

Yet probably it was inevitable. The reluctance of large Japanese firms to resort to layoffs under even severe business pressure for social reasons "is a formidable problem," acknowledges Armacost. "These are structural issues that will weaken Japan-based companies, particularly those that compete in the outside world. You'd better show increasing rates of return . . . on those things which stimulate the flow of international capital to your enterprise, because those are the metrics those markets will use to judge both [your] success and their continuing support."

In other words, voluntarily sustaining the high fixed costs of a largely inflexible and very expensive Japanese labor aggregate lowers that rate of return. And therefore is a handicap that international Japanese enterprises may no longer find it possible to bear.

Japan is changing. And part of the change is that in many ways, its business base is continuing to erode. The advantages offered to its international enterprises are fading. Toshiba's factories are moving overseas to gain cost advantages (see Chapter 27); its in-house companies are moving out and closer to their global customers to gain market; the strategic plan is for the corporation to go on expanding its overseas business. How long can it be before the question begins to reverberate on the executive floor: why does the Toshiba Corporation need to ground itself in Japan at all?

MANAGING RISK

There are other liabilities that come with a global business territory that relies heavily on domestic base, Toshiba has learned. One is the volatility of currency exchange rates: in mid 2001, a rise in the value of Japan's currency against the dollar by a single yen computed to a loss in profits of 12.5 million dollars to Toshiba.[2] In the last part of 2001 the exchange rate was moving by as much as two full yen per week, though mainly staying in the range of slightly above 120 to 1 dollar.

But the heaviest, most disheartening blow to fall on Toshiba from the global environment recently had really little to do with where it manufactures, but much more to do with how Toshiba has apprehended the risks of doing business across this now wide-opened frontier, and prepared for them.

The case had nothing to do with any smuggling in Asia or transfer-tax squabbles in Europe. It had to do with the highly controversial American tradition of the class-action lawsuit. Through this type of litigation, one or several plaintiffs can file suit against any company, US or foreign, on behalf of a non-participating "class" of people, ranging into hundreds of thousands in number, who are asserted to be "victims" of some knowing or careless failure on the part of the defendant, the company.

It's a high-stakes maneuver, as Toshiba learned painfully in 1999 when two plaintiffs launched a class-action lawsuit against the company over the claim of a faulty floppy-disk-drive controller chip that could, under extreme conditions, possibly destroy data written on the disk. Neither those two plaintiffs nor any other members of the "class" suing Toshiba demonstrated that such a thing had ever happened with a Toshiba computer.

But if Toshiba had pushed the suit to a jury trial for resolution, and lost, the company could have been forfeit a staggering 8.8 billion dollars in "compensation." Because of "the special situation in the United States in which a defendant may lose only because there is the possibility, albeit theoretical, of damage occurring, even though no such cases of damage have been reported,"[3] and even though, as Armacost puts it, "the company did a wonderful job of saying they would replace anything for anybody [to make the machines right]," Toshiba decided to settle, without admitting wrongdoing, at a cost of about one billion dollars.

Then-President Nishimuro said, "If we had fought and lost, it would have threatened the future of the company, so we choked back our tears and decided to settle."[4]

"Two things I have to say" in retrospect, says Chairman Nishimuro of the bitter experience now. "One is we should have been more careful about the proceedings of the US legal practices – we should have reacted much more speedily. And the other is, there is a problem with the small IC circuitry. As technology progresses, and it does progress very rapidly, we should have revisited what we had developed in the past. That feedback system was not established. But it is now.

"But [this kind of] risk in staying in the US always remains. We have to make sure to stay clear of every risk we can imagine. But always risk comes out of the blue."

It's one more condition – being ready to protect the brand under completely unforeseeable circumstances – of doing business in "the global game," and Toshiba learned it in a very hard way.

NAMES OF THE GAMES

What comes first, the product – or the brand? In the case of Toshiba, with its tens of thousands of products and now services growing by the dozens, it's a very hard problem, perhaps a critical one, to even think about. The more so because Toshiba, at 127 years old, had never really, along the way, stopped to do that. In Japan, everybody just knew what Toshiba was: one of the biggest corporations in the country, and the maker of damned good motors.

Perhaps it was the class-action suit, perhaps it was a realization provided by a consultant – but by mid 2000, the need to find a foundation for Toshiba's name as a corporate brand became apparent enough that President Okamura convened a task force to consider what should be done.

What needed to be done was the creation of a Corporate Brand Management Division, to the command of which was shortly appointed Mr. Koji Hase: one of the Toshiba wizards of DVD (see Chapter 15).

"Throughout my 30 years with Toshiba, in most cases I thought this company is abusing its brand name, and its trademark. It just was not fostering the brand intentionally and strategically."

Sony. IBM. Kodak. McDonald's. What do we know about those names? We know they're famous for making certain things. What does Toshiba make? A whole lot of stuff . . .

But there's a question more basic than that to start with, Hase feels. "What *is* a brand? It's a kind of promise that this company, Toshiba, is going to deliver something to you. This is the value you are purchasing: it may be the functionalities of a television, it may be benefit of the pride that comes with owning a Toshiba, it may enrich your information life at home or in the office. It's the promise of what it is that we will deliver."

Fine. But Toshiba delivers thousands of "promises," and still more complexly, spread across three customer domains: industrial, consumer, and technological. So what's the promise — that the things it makes will, respectively, add value? Bring enjoyment? Be the most advanced? Or some combination?

How would you put all that on a billboard?

Hase has only had his job since April 2001, but his background merging the DVD allies gave him a good head start on sensing how people feel about things. Lest he trust too much those instincts of his own, the first mission was to poll the 845 companies that all use the Toshiba brand – on anything from esoteric services to simple batteries. From those answers, he learned what he'd already guessed: it's a diversified firm. "It's so diversified that therefore there is no way we can crystallize our value to certain customers." He was afraid that would happen.

Not afraid, really. Just confirmed in his suspicions that "branding for Toshiba will take years. It will take years. And whatever I do, it will take some substantial business model to begin with. Without that, branding is nothing." You've got to know what it is the customer *wants* you to promise.

There have been some suggestions from higher on the corporate ladder. Senior Executive Vice President Yasuo Morimoto has done some thinking too. "Our brand ranking is just not high enough, only perhaps seventh or so in Japan. Of course that's not acceptable. One of the answers may be to introduce a brand fee system.

"Monetarize the brand, I mean. We have over 800 affiliated companies; we should recognize the brand ought not to be free of charge. It should be compensated for by users like our in-house companies."

Morimoto's suggestion has the virtue of reasonable assumption that a user licensing the brand for money will think very carefully of how to use it most effectively among customers and prospects it knows well, to strengthen sales no matter what the product.

It still would leave Hase with the ticklish problem of how to integrate all those tactics into a single corporate-brand strategy. He does have tools. There are ten people in his newly created office, and he has a budget with which to travel, ask questions, formulate the answers, proselytize the organization at many levels.

The president is squarely in his corner, having created the new Corporate Brand Management Division as a division that reports to the president himself, and having spearheaded a decision to purchase the title of "Official IT Partner" of FIFA World Cup Soccer for the next six years (covering the 2002 FIFA World Cup Korea/Japan™ and the 2006 FIFA World Cup Germany™), to give Hase a canvas on which to paint.

But at bottom Hase really confronts two severe quandaries. First is that, having historically ignored brand management, Toshiba comes now very late to a very crowded brand environment: the international marketplace. GE, Philips, Siemens, IBM, Panasonic, Dell, Maytag, Motorola, even Samsung – all have carved out spaces for their names, that all project their images well into Toshiba's product territories. There may be room now for no more "concept" brands, but only for advertising slogans.

Second is the globalization of Toshiba's world. Hase has to keep up with the fact that the reorganization of Toshiba itself – what businesses it will and won't be in, whether the in-house companies will shrink to eight or grow to thirteen next year, in the medium term or in the far future – is still undecided. Never mind his real need to understand the dynamics of the competitive situation just now in all the new foreign markets where Toshiba is headed.

Hase helped launch a revolution years ago, by looking for a new product for a new age. He found it in DVD. Now he has to find a way to explain that a new player is on the world stage. Not just something like a collection of always-on Japanese factories with more products to hustle, but some*one*.

And he's got to say why it matters, to you, to use, to know Toshiba and understand it. Of course it won't be easy, but he is being given the backing of the whole corporation itself – because the man in the captain's chair, Tadashi Okamura, believes the priority ranks that high.

As the president himself put it with some passion at the start of the new and very challenging year 2002, "It has been said that Toshiba's businesses are very diversified, and so too difficult to focus on sufficiently. Some securities analysts have even said that as long as Toshiba remains so diversified, they will avoid our shares. I must disagree.

"I take this diversification in an era of such structural change as we are now in to be an advantage, since all industries and all players are casting about for ways to redirect their own businesses in the face of the IT revolution.

"Our challenge is not to abandon Toshiba's businesses simply because there are so many, but rather to evolve them within an open structure, in which integration will be a vital factor. More than that, the integration of our businesses to serve customers with new products in new ways will be a developmental process of global collaboration. Globalization is now more than ever not just some plan of one company expanding worldwide, but a strategy of forging, with all the technological and business tools we have, win-win relationships with the winners of each region. That too influences what we stand for.

"Let me tell you what I think is happening to us, to make Toshiba's strategy viable for victory in the long term. We still have not entered the full phase of the IT revolution, which has only begun. The beginning, and its setbacks, are unfortunately being identified as a 'bust' – but the truth is that we are now ready for the second phase of an IT revolution – because just using more computers and cell phones was never the true revolution in the first place.

"The next phase of the revolution comes from now, with the reorganization of communications carriers and application service providers, the migration of standard Internet business models from business-to-customer to business-to-business, and the settlement on new technologies and new infrastructure to support these changes. That is when the real economy and the Internet economy will begin truly merging.

"Right now, though a top priority is a recovery in our business results, the truly vital thing is for us to change our corporate culture to meet this revolution. Through my communication with people throughout Toshiba, I have come to realize that, although we share a sense of crisis, it has so far been channeled into a general uncertainty about the future . . . and not enough in the direction of generating support for reform. With an understanding that the time has come to part ways with the old corporate culture, we next need to deepen communication on all fronts, break down organizational barriers and hierarchy, to create an efficient and open culture.

"I have asked everyone on my managerial team to drastically change their working style, to take an active role in communicating with the market and their colleagues, and to help me see the technology assets of Toshiba Group turned into shared resources, so that everyone can work towards building the new answers to the next part of the revolution, towards building new competitiveness.

"We, Toshiba people, must keep always in our minds that only those who succeed in their planned reforms will prevail as winners in the end. And when we do succeed, then the world will see indeed that Toshiba stands for commitment to people, for the new age and the ages that follow."

NOTES

1. Michael E. Porter, Hirotaka Takeuchi, Mariko Sakakibara, *Can Japan Compete?*, Perseus Publishing, Cambridge MA, 2000
2. "Exporters take currency risk by the throat," *Nikkei Weekly*, 16 July 2001
3. "Japanese firms growing wary of 'American risk,'" *Yomiuri Daily News*, 10 November 1999
4. *Yomiuri Daily News*, ibid.

Chronology

1875   Hisashige Tanaka opened a telegraph equipment factory in Shimbashi, Tokyo.

1890   Ichisuke Fujioka and Shoichi Miyoshi established Hakunetsu-sha & Co., Ltd. in Kyobashi, Tokyo. Manufactured Japan's first electric incandescent light bulbs.

1894   Produced Japan's first waterwheel power generators (60kW). Manufactured Japan's first electric fans.

1895   Produced Japan's first induction motors.

1899   Hakunetsu-sha & Co. renamed Tokyo Electric Co.

1911   Started to use the trade name "Mazda."

1915   Manufactured Japan's first X-ray tubes.

1919   Produced Japan's first radio vacuum transmission tubes.

1921   Invented the "double coil electric bulb," one of the six great inventions in bulb technology.

1924   Started trial manufacture of cathode-ray tubes. Manufactured Japan's first radio receivers.

1930   Manufactured Japan's first electric washing machines and refrigerators.

1931   Released Japan's first vacuum cleaners.

1936   Completed Japan's first 150kW broadcast transmitter for NHK (Japan Broadcasting Corporation).

1939   Tokyo Electric Company merged with Shibaura

Engineering Works Co., Ltd. and established Tokyo Shibaura Electric Co., Ltd.

Completed five units of the world's largest waterwheel power generators (100,000kW).

1940   Manufactured Japan's first fluorescent lamps.

1949   Developed Japan's first 1,500A–1,000kW unipolar mercury rectifiers.

1952   Completed Japan's first TV broadcast transmitters and TV microwave relay system.

1953   Manufactured Japan's first 72,500 kVA umbrella-type waterwheel generators.

1954   Developed TAC, Japan's first digital computer, for the University of Tokyo.

1955   Released Japan's first electric rice cookers.

1957   Completed aurora radars for Antarctic observation and radars to observe scattering phenomena.

1959   Developed Japan's first transistorized televisions.
        Developed Japan's first microwave ovens.

1960   Established Toshiba Musical Industries Co. (renamed Toshiba-EMI, Ltd.).

1961   Established corporate research & development center.

1962   Adopted "Toshiba" trademark in place of "Mazda."

1963   Completed Japan's first 12,500kW nuclear power turbine generators.
        Developed transmitters for satellite communications.

1964   Completed one of the world's largest centralized remote-control monitoring systems at electrical substations for Tokaido Shinkansen Bullet Trains.

1967   Developed the world's first automatic mail-code reader.

1968   Developed a 100,000 Gauss superconducting magnet, the most powerful in Japan.

1970   Developed the world's first color video phone.

1971   Released the world's first expanded IC color televisions.

1972   Completed Japan's first 700,000kW turbine generator. Released the world's first color television with black stripe-type cathode-ray tubes.

1973   Completed a 110,000kW geothermal power plant, the world's largest.

1975   Celebrated 100th anniversary. Completed 1-million kW turbine generator, the largest in Japan.

1977   Developed the world's fastest high-speed whole-body CT scanner.

1978   Launched medium-sized experimental broadcast satellite, Yuri. Released the first Japanese word processor.

1979   Developed world's first optical-disk-based data filing systems.

1982   Developed Japan's first Magnetic Resonance Imaging systems (MRI).

1983   Commercialized the world's first OCR technology able to read Chinese characters. Developed excimer-laser etching technology for very large-scale integration (VLSI) devices.

1984   Completed new head office, Toshiba Building. Started operation of experimental 50kW fuel cell power plant, the largest in Japan.

1985   Developed Japan's first transceiver for High-Definition TV systems. Developed 1-megabit CMOS DRAM. Introduced world's first laptop computers.

1989   Introduced world's first notebook computer, DynaBook.

1991   Developed the world's first 4-megabit NAND-type Electrically Erasable and Programmable Read-only Memory (EEPROM).

1993   Produced prototype product of the world's smallest MOS transistor, with a gate length of 0.04 microns.

1994   Introduced the sub-notebook personal computer, DynaBook SS.

1995   Developed high-density optical disk, DVD. DVD standardized.

1996   Introduced the mini-notebook computer, Libretto. Introduced DVD video players and DVD-ROM drives.
Formed Solid-State Floppy-Disk Card (SSFDC) Forum with Fuji Photo Film, Sega Enterprises, Olympus Optical and Tokyo Electron to promote SmartMedia as de facto standard.

1997   Developed manufacturing prototype of super-slim low-temperature polysilicon TFT LCD.

1998   Developed the world's first MPEG 4 graphical data compression and expansion LSI.
Formed the Bluetooth Special Interest Group with Ericsson, IBM, Intel and Nokia to promote Bluetooth technology.
Established Towani Corporation with Nippon Television Network and Warner Bros. to produce and distribute movies and television programs for the global market.

1999   Formed the SD Association with Matsushita Electric Industrial and SanDisk to promote SD Memory Card.
Spun off Air Conditioning Equipment Division to a joint-venture company with Carrier, Toshiba Carrier Corporation.
Introduced in-house company system.

Launched the world's quietest MRI.

Developed the world's fastest 128-bit CPU.

2000 Celebrated 125th anniversary.

Established FlashVision LLC with SanDisk to produce advanced flash memory.

Established ePF Network Corporation with Matsushita Electric Industrial and Hitachi for e-Platform standardization.

Commercialized the world's first Bluetooth-enabled product.

2002 Established a joint venture with Matsushita Electric Industrial to unify LCD business.

Index